P9-CAN-721

the telescope and the world of astronomy

THE TELESCOPE AND THE WORLD OF ASTRONOMY

By

Marvin F. Riemer, B.Ch.E., M.S.

Too low they build, who build beneath the stars.

Edward Young

SECOND EDITION
REVISED AND ENLARGED
1966

Published by

WOODSIDE, N.Y.

Library of Congress Catalogue No. 66-19355

311-66

Manufactured in Japan

TABLE OF CONTENTS

Appendix I Tables and Charts

Appendix II Constellation Maps For The Stellar Year

TABLE OF ILLUSTRATIONS

PHOTOGRAPHS PAGE

FIGURES PAGE

INTRODUCTION

ASTRONOMY, in common with most sciences, encompasses a vast and constantly increasing body of information. It is very likely that no one student can hope to master all, or even a large part, of this complex science with its deep-rooted bases in physics and mathematics. Indeed, as astronomical knowledge becomes more and more specialized, we find that the astrophysicist, for instance, may speak and think along very different lines from the radio-astronomer.

The enthusiastic amateur, with a brand-new telescope, who wants to explore the mysteries of the sky without prolonged study and with a minimum of delay, may profitably use the *Work Program For Beginners* included in the Appendix of the book (pages 161-162). This step-by-step approach can serve as a guide for the novice, who is understandably eager to turn his instrument to the glittering heavens.

The fundamentals of this science may prove somewhat confusing to the beginner. For that reason, he should consult especially Chapters II and V, where a simple presentation is made of all the data and knowledge that is needed for successful observations.

By following the work program outlined and by reference to this book, to other publications, and to star charts and atlases, the amateur will soon develop the basic skills which will admit him to the fraternity of those who look to the stars — the last frontier for modern man.

CHAPTER I

THE ETERNAL WONDER OF THE SKY

Naught is seen in the vault on high
But the moon, and the stars, and
the cloudless sky.

Joseph Rodman Drake

I. THE ETERNAL WONDER OF THE SKY

Astronomy — The Oldest Science

SINCE the beginning of time, men have turned their eyes upward to the arching dome of the heavens — and wondered. What man wonders about, he tries to explain. These explanations, a curious mixture of scientific observation and soaring imagination, constitute the science we call astronomy.

Man's earliest attempts to explain his universe may cause us to smile today, and yet those crude interpretations were supremely logical in view of man's limited picture of his own world. The earth *does* appear to be flat and the heavens *do* seem to be like a huge inverted bowl resting on the flat disc of the land below. Most of the primitive images of the universe were based on this seemingly logical view.

The apparent movement of the heavenly bodies across the sky is fairly obvious even to the casual observer. The Sun moves across the sky in the same way, day after day, rising in the east and setting in the west. The movement is the same although the Egyptians believed it to be the fiery boat of their Sun god sailing through the heavens, while the Greeks thought of it as the progress of Apollo's flaming chariot across the sky. And at night, the Moon can be seen to travel a similar path across the darkened sky — westward, always westward.

But what of the stars? Do they also move in great westward arcs as they wheel slowly overhead?

The ancient sky-watchers were well acquainted with the stars. They gave many of them individual names and they knew the fixed patterns of the constellations, which they saw as strange mythical beasts, as kings, and heroes. They knew that the stars moved, and always, in the nightly journey across the sky, along the well-worn trail to the west.

The ancient Greeks, who laid the foundations for much modern scientific inquiry, created a picture of the universe that lasted for two thousand years.

They explained the motion of the heavenly bodies by considering the Earth to be enclosed in an enormous, revolving, hollow globe whose inner surface was dotted and spangled with the glittering stars. Thus, as they looked upward and saw the stars move in slow, orderly procession overhead, they attributed this movement to the regular revolution of the celestial sphere that surrounded them. This concept of the universe is called the Ptolemaic theory after the Greek philosopher, Claudius Ptolemaeus (Ptolemy), who was the principal spokesman for this viewpoint.

The Early Astronomers

The geocentric theory, which fixed the Earth at the center of a gyrating, encircling universe, held sway over the minds of men until the middle of the sixteenth century when a mighty struggle began which ended in the complete destruction of the Ptolemaic view. The chief architect of this scientific revolution was Nicolaus Copernicus. This Polish cleric, with a deep interest in astronomy, could not reconcile his celestial observations and calculations with the accepted Ptolemaic construction of the universe. He was finally forced to discard the concept that the entire universe revolved majestically about the fixed Earth. By considering the Earth as merely another heavenly body that *moved* as did all the others, Copernicus was able to picture a universe more in accord with that indicated by his observations and mathematical computations: a universe where the Earth was but one member of a family of planets that revolved about a central Sun. He wrote, "But, if one should admit that the heavens possess none of this motion, but that the *Earth* rotates from west to east; and if one should consider this seriously with respect to the seeming rising and setting of the Sun, of the Moon, and the stars; then one would find that it is actually true."

Copernicus knew that his theory would create a furor when it burst upon the world — a world where clerical authority was supreme in deciding virtually all questions, where to cast doubt upon ecclesiastical doctrine might result in death by burning — a heretic's death.

But Copernicus was a cautious man. His great book which outlined his theory, *Concerning The Revolution Of The Heavenly Bodies*, was, by his order, not published until his death was imminent in 1543. Copernicus had not underestimated the effect of his revolutionary theory. The publication of his book launched a controversy that seethed among philosophers for more than a century.

Support for the Copernican theory was slow in coming. The full weight of canonical authority, which was committed to the Ptolemaic view, was used to suppress the new doctrine. Giordano Bruno was burned at the stake for holding, among other beliefs, that the Earth moved as Copernicus said.

In time, however, the observations of other astronomers began to amass a wealth of evidence that tended to vindicate Copernicus. Foremost among these observers was Tycho Brahe, a Dane, whose interest in the movements of the planets and the stars arose, curiously enough, from his belief in astrology. He was a magnificent observer, however, and his measurements of planetary motions and his star charts were marvels of precision, considering that the telescope was as yet unknown and measuring instruments relatively crude.

The fascinating Tycho Brahe died in 1601 leaving his superb collection of astronomical data to the brilliant mathematician-astronomer, Johannes Kepler. Kepler knew that Tycho's measurements and observations did not agree *exactly* with the Copernican theory of circular planetary movement about the Sun. For years he attempted to resolve this curious puzzle, and in the end he was successful.

The planets did not move around the Sun in circular paths as Copernicus had thought, but rather in flattened circles or ellipses. Kepler now could show that, with the planets moving in elliptical orbits, Tycho Brahe's measurements were more nearly in accord with the Copernican theory. Kepler's Laws of Planetary Motion provided an unshakeable mathematical argument for the views of Copernicus as opposed to Ptolemy.

It was the great scientific investigator, Galileo Galilei, who added the weight of visual evidence to the mathematical evidence that buried the Ptolemaic concept forever. The telescope was invented in 1608 and Galileo lost no time in turning an instrument of his own construction to the heavens. It was a crude instrument, merely a paper cylinder and a pair of simple lenses, but Galileo was no crude observer. What he saw strengthened his belief in the Copernican view. The crowning piece of evidence was the brilliant observations he made of the motions of four of Jupiter's moons. Night after night he watched the tiny satellites shift their positions as they revolved around the giant planet. It was this evidence of an ordered motion in the solar system that led him to support the Copernican theory.

Although Galileo was later forced by clerical pressure to recant his view, we may take as his true belief his statement that, "Our sense of sight presents to us four satellites circling about Jupiter, like the Moon about the Earth, while the whole system travels over a mighty orbit about the Sun."

Why the planets travel as they do is the question answered by Sir Isaac Newton. The forces of attraction between bodies, the forces of gravitation, explain in simple mathematical terms why the Moon moves in its particular path around the Earth; and the Earth, in turn, in its undeviating orbit around the Sun. Newton's Laws of Motion and his theory of gravitation ushered in the modern era of astronomy. The Earth was no longer considered the central focus of the universe but merely one of nine planets revolving around one of a million stars. Man's place in the scheme of things had changed and astronomers now moved forward to define this new universe.

Astronomy Today

The modern astronomer explores a larger and more mysterious universe than that which occupied his predecessors. His basic approach is the same: — relying strongly on observation, mathematical calculations, and disciplined imagination. Today, in addition, he has equipment of great precision and new design.

Telescopes have improved tremendously since Galileo fixed a pair of lenses at either end of a hollow tube. Sir Isaac Newton invented an entirely new kind of telescope by dispensing with lenses and substituting a curved reflecting mirror instead. The larger modern telescopes are of this reflecting mirror type, the giant of them all being the 200-inch mirror at the Mount Palomar Observatory in California. This telescope permits the astronomer to probe into the depths of space beyond the wildest imaginings of Galileo.

The 200-inch Hale Reflecting Telescope, as it is called, is located on top of Palomar Mountain, near San Diego, California. The huge mirror and its delicately balanced mounting are magnificent examples of craftsmanship and engineering skill. The photograph on page 21 provides some idea of the immense dome of the observatory and the telescope framework within.

Light which reaches us after journeying across the immense distances of stellar space is often too dim to be recorded by the human eye. The modern astronomer, therefore, substitutes a highly sensitive photographic film and makes long time exposures to record the faint emanations of light from stars invisible to the human eye. Astro-photography reveals unsuspected new information about our universe. The serious amateur can increase his pleasure in astronomical observations tenfold by learning to use his camera in conjunction with his telescope as he explores the sky.

In the great observatories, light from the distant stars is often directed not onto a photographic plate, but, rather, into a marvelous instrument called a spectroscope. We all know that white light is made up of a specific array of colored components. A prism, which is basically a triangular slab of glass, will split such a beam of white light into

Figure 1. Prism resolving beam of white light into a spectrum

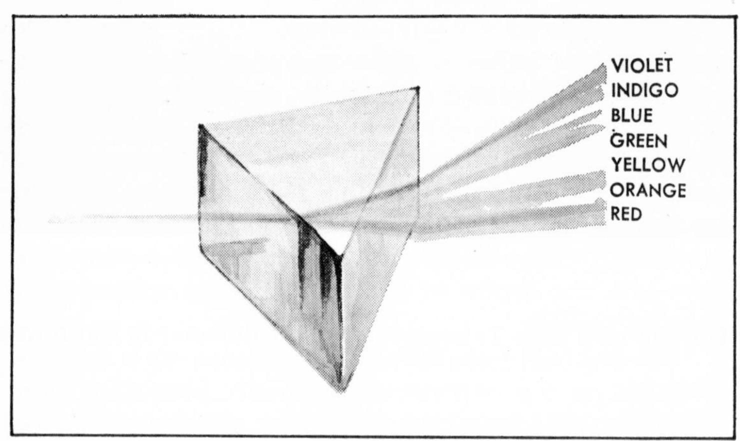

Photograph from the Mount Wilson and Palomar Observatories.

The 200-inch Hale Telescope at Mount Palomar in California.

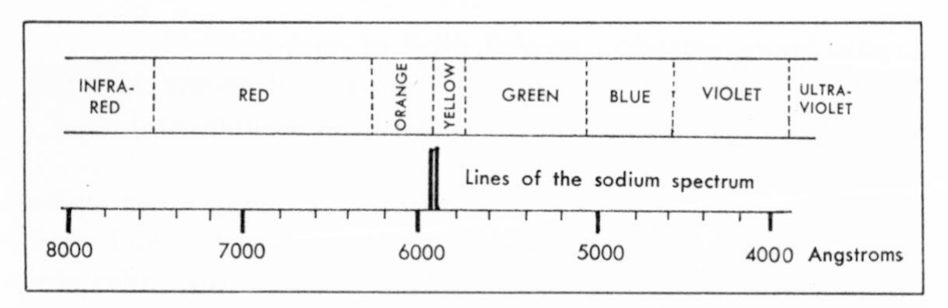

Figure 2. Sodium "Fraunhofer" lines in position on spectrum

a rainbow of colors — the spectrum. See Figure 1. This phenomenon was first demonstrated by Sir Isaac Newton.

While experimenting with the spectra of light, a German scientist named Fraunhofer found that light from a specific source had a distinctive spectrum all its own. For instance, burning sodium will show, superimposed on the spectrum, a pair of dark lines at a specific wave-length and no other element will exhibit the same pattern. See Figure 2. Each chemical element, then, has an individual spectral design — the Fraunhofer lines, as they are called — that identifies the chemical element as surely as a fingerprint identifies a man.

Now, in the spectroscope, the astronomer has an instrument that can analyze the light from the far reaches of the universe. By studying the spectra of the light from remote stars, he can catalogue the chemical elements of which they are composed. The spectroscope tells him what the distant worlds are made of.

The newest technique employed in mapping the heavens involves the use of huge parabolic radio antennas which can pick up "radio noise", the sounds of deep space. These radio-telescopes can be aimed quite accurately at a specific point in the sky and the source of the emission of radio waves can be pinpointed. It has been demonstrated that many celestial bodies give off radio waves, including stars, star clusters, nebulae, galaxies, the Sun, and even our neighboring planets. It should not be imagined that this radio wave emission is any kind of communication. It is, rather, much like "static" in nature and seems to be the result of the interaction of masses of clouds and dust in space.

The great advantage of radio-astronomy over optical astronomy is that while light waves can be blocked off by interfering masses of stellar debris and gas, the radio emissions easily penetrate this "space fog" in the same manner that radio waves from a broadcasting station are not blocked by the walls of the listener's home. Much new information is being gleaned about our universe from the "baby" science of radio-astronomy.

The largest radio-telescope is at Jodrell Bank in England. The huge, bowl-shaped network of steel that makes up this antenna has a diameter of 250 feet. The largest American radio-telescope is located at Green Bank, West Virginia. It measures 85 feet across. The United States Navy is now constructing a titan of radio-telescopes. At Sugar Grove, West Virginia, an antenna, as big as two football fields laid end to end, 600 feet across, will allow radio-astronomers to intercept radio waves from sources that are 350,000,000,000,000 miles from the mountains of West Virginia.

CHAPTER II

EQUIPMENT FOR SKY-WATCHERS

It is not accident that wherever we point the telescope we see beauty, that wherever we look with the microscope there we find beauty. It beats in through every nook and cranny of the mighty world.

R. M. Jones

II. EQUIPMENT FOR SKY-WATCHERS

THE SKY exerts a tremendous fascination for anyone who is interested in the universe that surrounds him. And yet some people fail to pursue this interest because of the belief that successful sky-watching requires elaborate and expensive equipment. This is by no means the truth. Observations made with the naked eye or with a pair of binoculars can be rewarding and exciting. Certainly the serious amateur will want to own a telescope, but worthwhile observations can be made and enjoyed with simpler equipment.

The Human Eye

The unaided human eye is capable of perceiving many of the wonders of the sky. No one has complained that he needed a telescope to see the fiery trace of a meteor streaking across the sky. The Moon, as it passes through its phases in the course of the month, is easily observed with the naked eye. Most important of all, perhaps, the patterns that the stars make in the sky are best studied without the aid of optical instruments. These star patterns, the constellations, are invaluable aids in finding one's way about the sky. They are the beacons, the guideposts, that point the way to specific stars and other celestial phenomena that attract the astronomer. Stars are always listed and catalogued with reference to the constellations in which they are seen.

It should be remembered that many of the stars and most of the constellations arching overhead were named by simple shepherds thousands of years before the invention of the telescope. The amateur astronomer should become familiar with the constellations that are visible from his vantage point on the Earth. The maps and star charts included in this book will prove to be helpful.

Binoculars

The sky-watcher who first turns a pair of binoculars to the heavens is in for a surprise. An entirely new perspective of the vast panorama of the sky unfolds. Our closest neighbor in space, the Moon, can be profitably studied through good binoculars. The larger craters and "seas" of our satellite can be readily seen. Many more stars will be revealed and some "double stars" can be successfully resolved with the aid of binoculars. A good pair of binoculars will permit the observer to retrace the work of Galileo, as the moons of Jupiter may be seen without difficulty. The hazy veil of the Milky Way will be revealed as a vast complex of stars and filmy masses of glowing clouds.

Binoculars for sky-watching should preferably be of 6 to 8 power. Binoculars are usually rated by a pair of figures, for example, "6 x 30" or "10 x 50". The first number of the pair indicates the magnifying power of the instrument. Thus, "6 x 30" means a binocular that magnifies six times and "10 x 50" will provide a magnification of ten times. The second number is the diameter in millimeters of the objective or front lens; it is a measure of the light-gathering ability of the binoculars. For adequate light-gathering power the size of the objective should be about five times the magnifying power. Therefore a "7 x 35" glass is gathering sufficient light for effective observation while a "7 x 25" is not. A "7 x 50", often called a "night glass" has even more light-gathering power than a "7 x 35."

The amateur astronomer will find many uses for a good pair of prism binoculars. (Prisms are light bending devices which direct the light from the widely separated front objectives to the rear eyepieces which are set more closely together.) The photograph below shows a pair of prism type binoculars.

Prism binoculars. Note socket for use with tripod at high power.

A "7 x 35" instrument would probably serve very nicely for general sky scanning. As a matter of fact, many authorities feel that a 7 power binocular represents the maximum magnification that can be successfully hand-held without excessive strain or quivering. Some people can handle 8 power binoculars but beyond this size a tripod or other support will prove helpful.

Telescopes

Most astronomical observing is done with a telescope.

There are many types of instruments available, and the arguments for or against a certain kind are always being waged when amateur astronomers get together. Actually, each type has certain advantages and disadvantages. Most kinds, however, will afford the beginning sky-watcher many hours of pleasure as he pursues his study of the sky.

In general, there are two types of telescopes: refracting telescopes and reflecting telescopes. The function of any telescope is to obtain a sharp, clear image by bringing rays of light to a point of focus. The refracting telescope uses a lens which bends the rays of light to meet at the focal point, while the reflecting telescope employs a curved mirror which reflects the light rays to meet at

Figure 3. Path of light rays in a refractor and a reflector

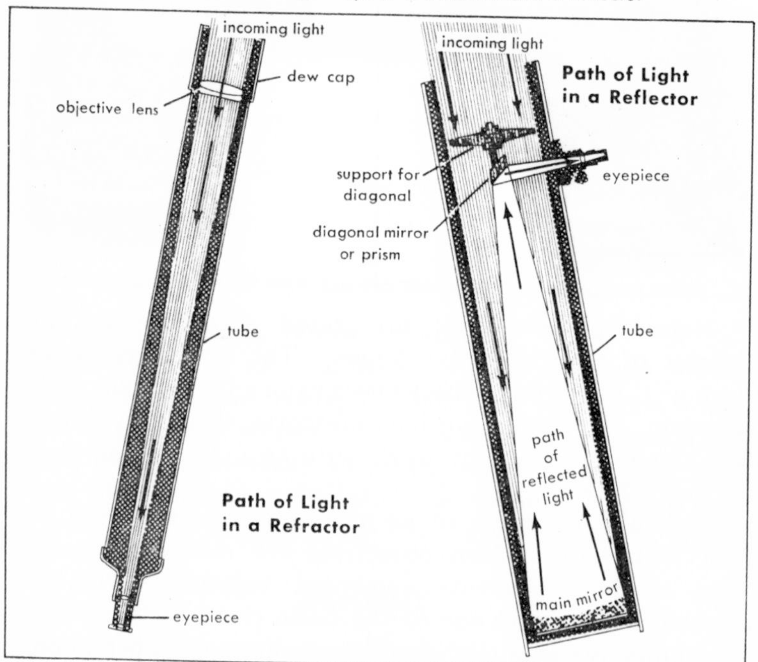

the point of focus. Figure 3 indicates the way in which light rays travel through the two types of telescopes. It will be noted that the light rays are brought to a point of focus at the eyepiece lens of the telescope. Both kinds of telescope do the same job but each in a different way.

Very simply, the refracting telescope consists of two lenses, one at each end of a tube. The objective lens serves to gather the light rays coming from a distant source, perhaps a star. Naturally, the larger the objective lens, the more light it can gather. The rays of light are bent by the objective lens to meet at a point of focus. The image at the focal point (the primary image) is then enlarged by the other lens, the eyepiece, which is, essentially, the magnifying lens of the telescope. See Figure 4.

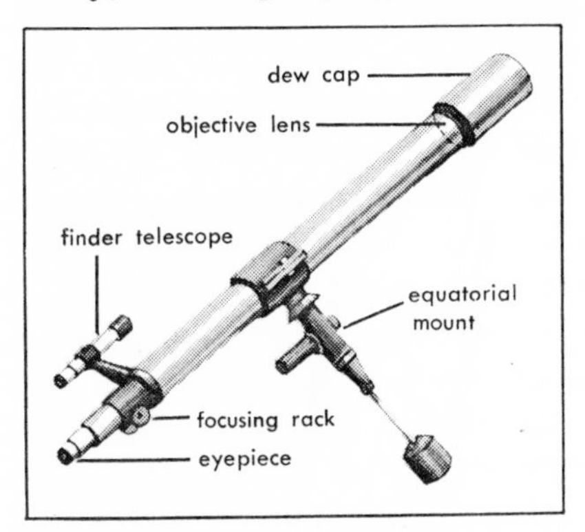

Figure 4. The Refracting Telescope

Refracting telescopes are rated according to the diameter of their objective lenses. The largest refractor in the world is at the Yerkes Observatory in Williams Bay, Wisconsin. The objective lens measures 40 inches across. Most amateurs, however, work with two, three, and four inch refractors.

Although we speak of an objective lens, it should be noted that most modern objectives are made of several lenses or lens elements cemented together. This is designed to eliminate one of the basic characteristics of a single objective lens, the quality of chromatic aberration.

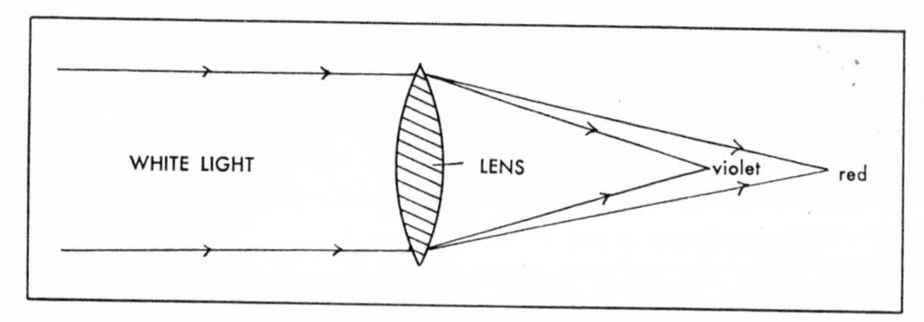

Figure 5. Light rays focused at different points resulting in chromatic aberration

This occurs as a result of the inability of the lens to focus light rays of different colors at the same focal point. Figure 5 shows that the lens, which also functions as a prism, disperses white light into its component colors. The violet component is refracted or bent the most; the red component, the least. The defect, known as chromatic aberration, causes the image to give off rings or halos of deceptive color. It was this phenomenon, largely eliminated in modern lenses, that led Sir Isaac Newton to invent the reflecting telescope.

A reflecting telescope, in essence, consists of an open tube with a curved mirror at the bottom. The open end of the tube is pointed at the object in the sky and the entering light rays strike the mirror at the bottom. The rays, reflected from the mirror, strike a second mirror called a flat or a diagonal. As a result of the curvature of the main mirror, the light rays are bent to meet at a point. The mirror in a reflecting telescope must be painstakingly ground to the proper curvature to achieve the correct focal point. The purpose of the diagonal mirror, which is located a short distance before the focal point, is to reflect the light rays toward the side of the tube where an eyepiece lens magnifies the image for the observer. See Figure 6.

There are several variations of this Newtonian reflector. The Cassegrain reflector has a hole in the

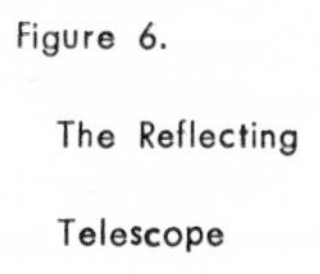

Figure 6.

The Reflecting

Telescope

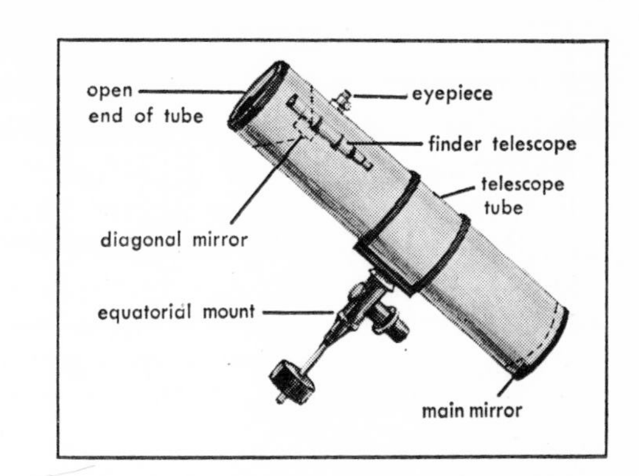

main mirror through which the light is reflected back by the flat mirror. The eyepiece in the Cassegrain is placed back of the hole in the main mirror. Another variation, the Herschelian reflector, eliminates the flat mirror altogether by tilting the main mirror in the tube to bring the focal point to the outside of the tube itself. Most reflectors are still built, however, on the principles exemplified in the Newtonian and they are all successful in the elimination of chromatic aberration.

Reflectors are rated by the diameter of their main mirror. This is a good indication of light-gathering power, but refractors and reflectors should not be compared inch for inch in rating them. By and large, a four-inch refractor is a far superior instrument to a four-inch reflector.

In comparing telescopes it must be kept in mind that reflectors are somewhat less expensive than refractors. In fact, if the amateur wishes to spend time and effort instead of money, he can grind his own mirror and make, if he is careful and precise, a fairly respectable instrument. The making of telescopes is beyond the scope of this book but some sources of information in this area may be found in the bibliography.

Reflecting telescopes require more care than refractors, and maintaining them in good order is something of a continuing chore. Mirrors must be resilvered after every two or three years of use. It is relatively rare to find that a refractor suffers from misalignment of lenses while reflector mirrors must be realigned almost as a matter of course.

It might also be mentioned that the eyepiece of a reflecting telescope is located at some distance up the side of the tube. This can, at times, make for uncomfortable or awkward viewing. Furthermore, the open tube of the reflector traps vagrant air currents and the resulting distortion of the image, although temporary, may be annoying.

In addition to the diameter of its objective lens or mirror, a telescope is classified by its *focal length.* This is the distance between the lens (or mirror) and the point where the light rays are brought to a focus — the focal point. If we divide the focal length by the diameter of the objective, we obtain the focal ratio, the "f/ number" so familiar to photographers. Thus, a 2.4 inch (60 mm.) refractor with a focal length of 35 inches (890 mm.) has a focal ratio of,

$$\frac{35}{2.4} = 14.6 \text{ or } f/\,14.6$$

Expressed in millimeters this would be,

$$\frac{890 \text{ mm}}{60 \text{ mm}} = f/\,14.8$$

The Quality Of A Lens

The quality of a lens is judged by considering a combination of three factors: light-gathering ability, magnifying power, and resolution. It is only by analyzing all of these component factors that we can determine whether the optics of a telescope can be relied upon to do an effective job.

The amount of light gathered by the telescope is

determined solely by the size of the objective lens or mirror. The larger the objective, the more light it will gather and the more clearly will the fainter objects in the sky be revealed. The light-gathering power of a lens increases as a square function of the lens diameter increase. Thus, a two-inch lens will gather four times as much light as a one-inch lens, and a three-inch lens will pick up nine times as much light as a one-inch lens.

The diameter of the aperture of the human eye is about 1/3 of an inch when the iris is expanded for night viewing. Therefore, a one-inch lens, which is three times larger than the eye diameter, will gather nine times as much light as the human eye. As the diameter of the objective increases, the light-gathering ability becomes much greater. The table which follows clearly demonstrates this relationship.

Diameter Of Objective Lens In Inches	Number Of Times More Light Gathering Power Than Human Eye
1″ (25 mm)	9
2″ (50 mm)	36
2.5″ (62 mm)	56
3″ (75 mm)	81
6″ (150 mm)	324
10″ (250 mm)	900

One of the first questions people ask on being confronted with a telescope is, "How much can it magnify?" The answer depends on two factors: the focal length of the objective lens (or mirror) and the focal length of the eyepiece. Only one calculation is needed to determine the power of magnification of a telescope. Simply divide the focal length of the objective by the focal length of the eyepiece.

$$\frac{\text{focal length of objective}}{\text{focal length of eyepiece}} = \text{magnification}$$

For example, a refractor with a focal length of 900 mm. may be used in combination with an eyepiece whose focal length is 40 mm.

$$\frac{900\text{ mm}}{40\text{ mm}} = 22.5$$

This eyepiece will produce an image magnification of 22.5 diameters and the tube of the eyepiece will be engraved "22.5 X" to indicate this.

Substituting another eyepiece of focal length of 9 mm., the magnification yielded would be:

$$\frac{900\text{ mm}}{9\text{ mm}} = 100$$

This eyepiece would produce a magnification of 100 X.

It will be readily seen that eyepieces with shorter focal lengths will provide greater magnification. An eyepiece with a focal length of 3 mm. will result in a magnifying power of

$$\frac{900\text{ mm}}{3\text{ mm}} = 300 \times \text{magnification}$$

For all practical purposes, however, telescope eyepieces are made in focal lengths of between 4 mm. and 60 mm.

If we try to increase magnification beyond certain limits we may expect some deterioration of image quality. Diffraction patterns appear and the image, though larger, is less distinct. At magnifications of about 60 times objective diameter, there is some loss in image sharpness although it is still possible to distinguish certain detail.

When we speak of the resolving power of a telescope lens, we mean its ability to demonstrate fine detail. Specifically, if two stars are so close together that the eye sees them as a single point of light, we must depend on the telescope to separate them into two individual components. This occurs as a result of the resolving power of the instrument.

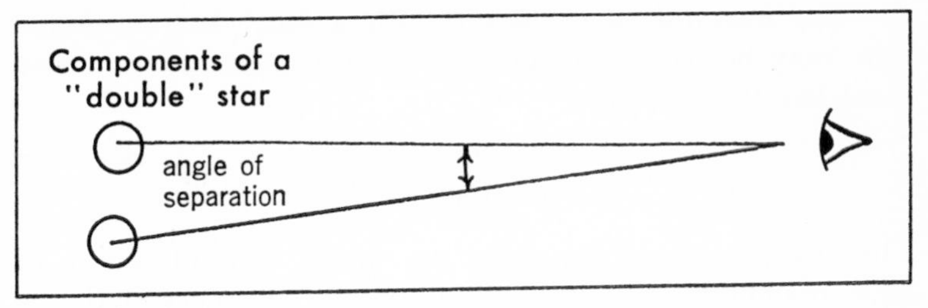

Figure 7. Measuring distances by angle of separation

This process of "splitting doubles" is one of the delights of the amateur astronomer. The ability of a telescope to resolve double stars is rated by a standard measure of resolution capacity — the Dawes Limit. This theoretical value is obtained by dividing the factor 4.5 by the diameter of the objective lens in inches. Thus, the Dawes Limit for a 2.5 inch lens would be:

$$\frac{4.5}{2.5} = 1.8$$

The Dawes Limit, 1.8, is expressed in *seconds of arc.*

Seconds of arc is the measure of an angle; there being in a right angle 90 degrees with each degree divided into 60 minutes and each minute into 60 seconds. One second of arc, then, is 1/3600th of a degree. How far the two stars of a "double" are separated from each other is measured by the seconds of arc of the angle of separation. See Figure 7.

Double Star	Separation sec./arc	Dawes Limit	Size of Objective Needed to "Split"
Alpha Herculis	4.7	4.5	1 inch
Castor........................	4.6	4.5	1 "
Epsilon Boötis............	2.8	2.3	2 "
Gamma Leonis	3.8	2.3	2 "
Delta Cygni	1.9	1.1	4 "
Eta Orionis	1.4	1.1	4 "

The Dawes Limit indicates, theoretically, the smallest angle of separation of two objects that a telescope is able to resolve into separate images. In actual practice a value of twice the Dawes Limit should be used to measure the working resolution of a telescope. Individual instruments under varying observational conditions may show some deviation from this figure. In the table on page 37 will be found several double stars, their angles of separation, Dawes Limit, and the size of objective lens diameter required to split these doubles. To locate the stars listed it will be necessary to refer to the star charts in the Appendix.

Eyepieces

The importance of the eyepiece lens in telescope performance cannot be minimized. Most telescopes are provided with several eyepieces of varying power, and the advanced amateur will probably want to add others to his collection.

The function of the eyepiece is to enlarge the image formed by the objective lens, and it is, therefore, a simple magnifier. Several types of eyepieces are available and each has certain specific characteristics and advantages.

The Huygens eyepiece is a two lens eyepiece widely used for low and medium power observations. It has fairly good color correction and represents a standard choice for most refracting and reflecting telescopes. The Ramsden is a somewhat similar eyepiece (with lenses reversed) and is often used interchangeably with the Huygens. An eyepiece with more lens elements and superior color correction is the Kellner, which provides as good a telescope image as can be obtained at medium powers. For high power observation (around 200X), the orthoscopic eyepiece is sometimes used. The orthoscopic is an excellent astro-eyepiece and is unsurpassed for very high magnifications.

The basic specifications of an eyepiece are usually engraved on the barrel. The type of eyepiece is indicated as well as the magnifying power. For instance, the notation, "H. 72 X", may be found. This means the eyepiece is a Huygenian with a magnifying power of 72 times. A table of common eyepiece types follows:

TYPES OF ASTRO-EYEPIECES

Symbol	Type	Characteristics
H.	Huygens	Paired plano-convex lenses. Good color correction. A standard astro-eyepiece.
H.M.	Huygens-Mittenzwey	A variation of the Huygenian with similar characteristics. Good lateral color correction in this eyepiece.
A.H.	Achromatic Huygenian	A Huygenian eyepiece which employs an achromatic eye lens resulting in better color correction.
R.	Ramsden	Paired plano-convex lenses. Slightly "flatter" field than Huygenian. Similar color correction, except for lateral color.
K.	Kellner	Consists of a plano-convex lens and a two-element achromatic eye lens. Some variations are found employing paired achromatic lenses (Plossl type). Large field, little chromatic aberration.
S.R.	Symmetrical	A pair of identical two-element achromatic lenses. Results in excellent color correction. A very good eyepiece for medium magnifications.
O.R.	Orthoscopic	Unsurpassed for high power work. A three-element field lens produces magnified images free from distortion and color aberration.
S.O.	Solid Ocular	Eyepiece made from a solid glass cylinder with ground ends. Good light transmitter with little distortion.
E.	Erfle	Three two-element achromatic lenses. Widest field of any eyepiece (50° to 70°).

It is tempting to use eyepieces of the highest power, but the best results are achieved by using the minimum magnification possible. With low power eyepieces larger areas of the sky can be observed and unfamiliar objects can be more easily found. In addition, at low power, objects can be seen more distinctly with greater clarity and sharpness. High power eyepieces not only reduce the field of view, but they also intensify the distortions and waverings produced by the disturbances in the atmosphere.

Telescope Accessories

There are many accessories that help to make sky-watching easier and more satisfying. As the amateur gains in experience, he will want to expand the area of his observations and attempt new projects. This will require some familiarization with the various kinds of telescope accessories that are available. In addition to the section which follows, a table of some of the more commonly used accessories will be found in the Appendix. It is suggested that the interested reader write for information on telescope accessories to Scope Instrument Corp., P.O. Box 1031, Woodside, N. Y. 11377.

One of the most important accessories (indeed, it is difficult to work effectively without one) is the telescope viewfinder. The finder is simply a miniature telescope mounted on the main telescope tube. Its purpose is to allow the observer to scan large areas of the sky to locate the object on which the main telescope is to be focused.

The finder telescope may be of 4, 6, or 8 power and it will have a wide field (5° or more) of view to facilitate searching for faint or unfamiliar objects. The eyepiece of the finder is usually fitted with a reticle (cross hairs) for more accurate positioning of sky objects. It is very important to adjust the finder so that the sky object centered in its cross hairs will be, likewise, centered in

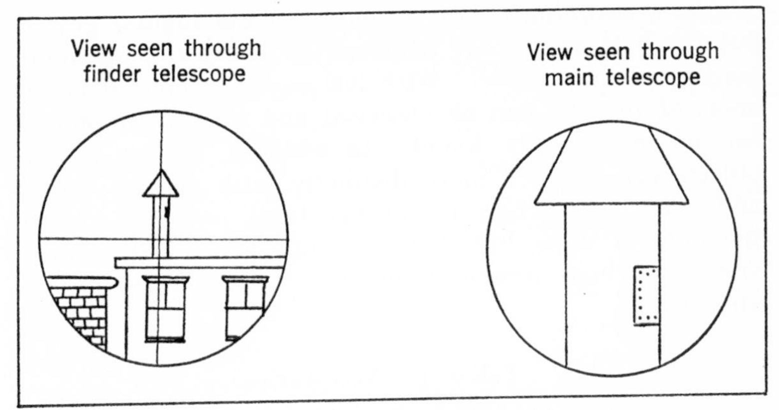

Figure 8. Alignment of The Viewfinder Telescope

the field of view of the main telescope.

It is best to make the adjustments of the finder in daylight as attempting the alignment on sky objects at night may prove confusing to the beginner. The finder should be aligned by sighting the telescope on some well-illuminated vertical terrestrial object, such as a fence post, telephone pole, or the corner of a building. The vertical line of the object that is sighted on should split the very center of the telescope field. The telescope mountings are then clamped tightly in position to prevent movement

Figure 9. The Star Diagonal

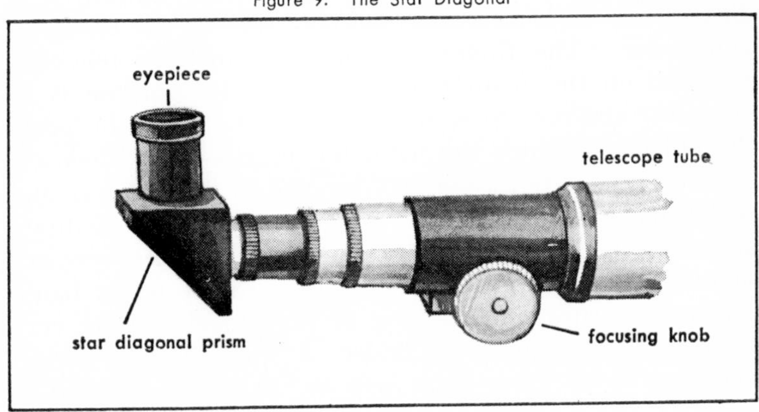

of the main telescope tube. Now the position of the object is checked in the field of the viewfinder telescope. If it is not "dead center" in the cross hairs, the finder is loosened in its mounting and carefully moved until the object is centered. Most finders are mounted by means of adjustable screws that permit the observer to make the proper adjustments. The image in the main telescope should then be checked again to see if it still remains centered in the field. In Figure 8, it will be seen that the finder is properly aligned with the main telescope as the object sighted upon is centered in the field of both telescopes. Note the reduced field of view that accompanies the increased magnification.

Some people consider the refracting telescope to be a "neckbreaker" because the observer, at times, in order to bring his eye to the line of sight of the eyepiece, must assume a strained position. This discomfort is eliminated by a very useful accessory — the star diagonal. See Figure 9.

The star diagonal consists of a prism which bends the light at right angles to the tube of the telescope so the observer can stand comfortably beside the tube while viewing. The eyepiece fits into the star diagonal and the path of the light rays through the star diagonal becomes part of the focal length of the objective lens. This permits using a shorter telescope tube and results in a more manageable instrument.

An accessory that is mandatory is some device that will protect the eyes when observing the Sun. If any observations are to be made of the Sun's disc, *it is absolutely necessary* to use a Sun filter or a Sun diagonal. The filter, or solar lens, is a heavily tinted glass disc that can be fitted to a telescope's eyepiece. The Sun diagonal is a special light absorbing prism. These precautions cannot be overemphasized as even a momentary glimpse of the Sun through the telescope, without proper protection, can cause permanent eye damage. Special techniques for making solar observations are discussed in detail in Chapter III.

The telescope, in common with many optical systems, produces an image that is inverted and reversed. In observing the sky this is no particular handicap and, as a matter of fact, the star diagonal turns the image right side up in the process of bending the light rays, although it does not reverse the image. However, if the telescope is to be used for land observations, then some device is needed to turn the image right side up and to reverse it as well. This may be done with either a prism or lens type image erecter. It should be noted that such a device should be reserved for terrestrial viewing as these image erecters reduce the amount of light reaching the observer's eye and are something of an encumbrance in celestial observation. For land viewing, however, the image erecter is a virtual necessity.

An accessory that many observers use to increase magnification is the Barlow lens. The Barlow lens is a simple concave lens in a tubular mounting, which is placed at some point in front of the focal point of the telescope objective. See Figure 10. A new image is formed at the greater focal length, thus increasing the magnification of the entire system. The eyepiece magnifies this new image and an increase in power of two or even three times is thus obtained.

Figure 10. The Barlow Lens

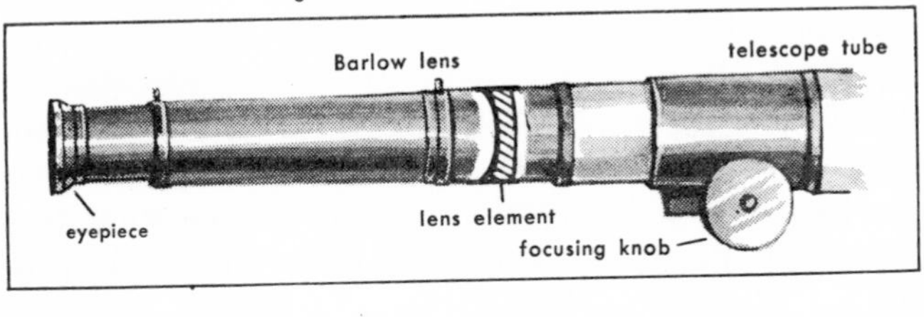

This means that the Barlow lens, in effect, doubles the number of eyepieces that are available to the observer.

With a 2X Barlow lens, for instance, and two eyepieces of 47X and 73X, four different magnifications are possible: 47X, 73X, 94X, and 146X.

The use of the Barlow lens tends to reduce the field of view somewhat, but it remains a simple and effective method of increasing telescope power. It should be remembered that, generally speaking, good observation technique suggests the use of the lowest power consistent with the demands of the particular observation that is being made.

Telescope Mounting

The mounting of the telescope has a considerable effect on the performance of the instrument. Obviously the mount must offer rigid support and yet it must be capable of smooth, controlled movements to guide the telescope as it "sweeps" the sky.

Two types of mounts are commonly employed on modern telescopes: the altazimuth mount and the equatorial mount. The altazimuth is the simpler of the two, and telescope movements can be made rapidly and smoothly. The name, altazimuth, is derived from the two motions of the telescope that this mount controls: an up and down motion — altitude, and a side-to-side movement — azimuth.

In the altazimuth mounting the telescope is held in a yoke or fork and moves around a horizontal pivot. The vertical component of the yoke rotates in a complete circle on a horizontal base. See Figure 11.

A good altazimuth mount will have locking devices on both the altitude and azimuth control mechanisms. In addition, the mounting may be fitted with "slow motions", which are controls designed to permit the observer to move the telescope smoothly over small distances while tracking a star.

The equatorial mount is somewhat more complicated than the altazimuth but it is a superior mount in many respects. It is especially valuable in following a specific star for an extended period of observation.

Although the apparent movement of the stars across the sky is slow, the telescope magnifies this motion and the observer will note that the star he is fixed on will slowly drift across the field of his telescope and disappear from view. To track the star the observer must use both of the slow motions on his altazimuth mount almost continuously or else the star will wander out of the field. The equatorial mount, on the other hand, permits following the star with but one simple adjustment of the telescope.

Figure 11.

The Altazimuth

Mount

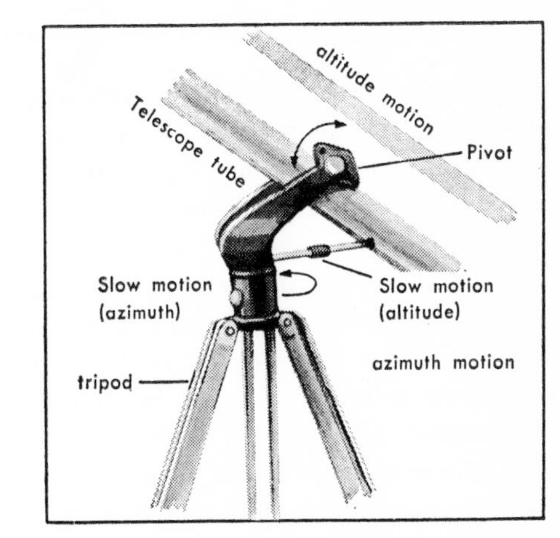

To understand why this is so and to help the sky-watcher understand something of the motion of the celestial bodies, it will be necessary to sketch out the "geography" of the heavens.

Mapping The Celestial Globe

The apparent motion of the stars from east to west is in a great circle around the celestial pole. We can see this circumpolar movement in certain astronomical photographs. In the photograph on page 135 it will be seen that

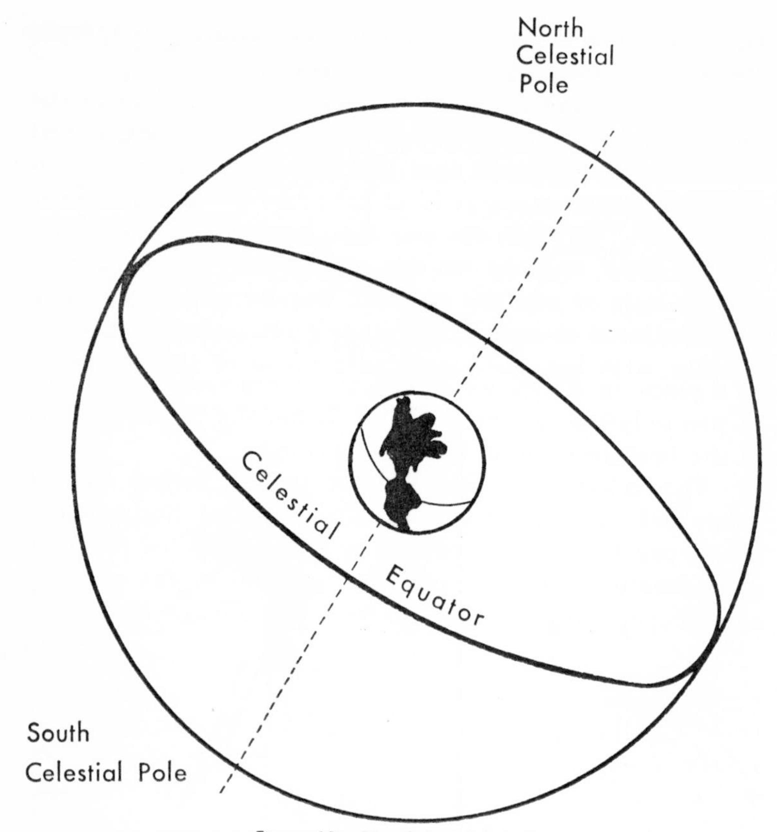

Figure 12. The Celestial Sphere

the star trails are circular arcs around the celestial pole as the time exposure recorded their paths on the film.

If we imagine the globe of the Earth to be enclosed within a far greater globe — the celestial sphere — then the projections of the Earth's poles and the Earth's equator on the greater celestial sphere will locate the celestial poles and the celestial equator. See Figure 12.

When mapping the globe of the Earth, we divide the sphere into parallels of latitude and meridians of longitude and, similarly, we scribe imaginary guide lines on the celestial sphere. If we are given the latitude and longitude

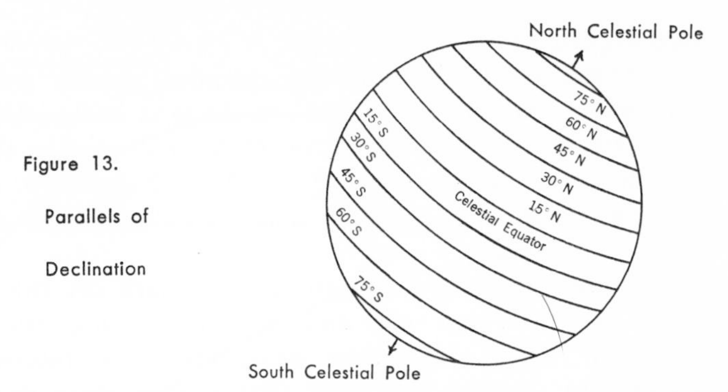

Figure 13.

Parallels of Declination

of a place on Earth, we can locate it precisely. And just as precisely we can locate a star in the sky by its position in the immense grid of the sky markings.

The celestial sphere, and let us not forget that it exists only in our imaginations, is divided horizontally, not by parallels of latitude, but by divisions called parallels of declination. These circles are parallel to the celestial equator and range from 0° to 90°. See Figure 13.

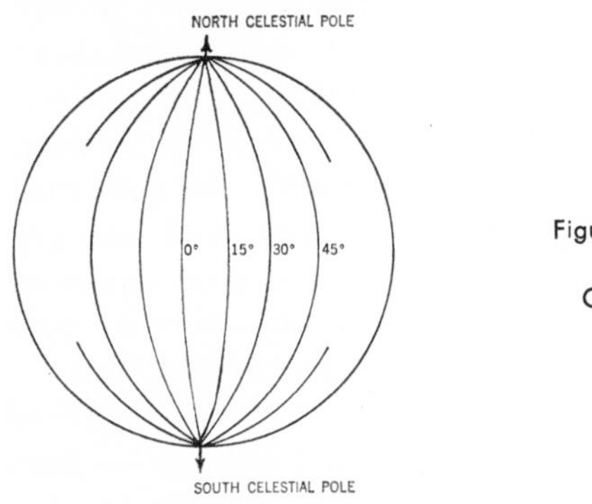

Figure 14.

Celestial Meridians

Declination measures the angular distance between any object in the sky and the celestial equator. We measure this declination in degrees, each degree containing 60 minutes and each minute 60 seconds.

The vertical divisions of the celestial sphere are great circles passing through the north and south celestial poles.

See Figure 14.

These circles divide the celestial sphere into 360° (degrees). At intervals of 15°, a circle is designated as an hour circle. This provides for 24 hour circles in the 360° of the celestial sphere ($\frac{360}{15} = 24$). Figure 15, looking downward at the celestial pole, illustrates this division into hour circles.

The meridians of longitude that mark off the Earth's globe are counted off and measured from the prime meridian which has been designated, by international agreement, as the meridian that passes through Greenwich, England, the site of the Royal Observatory. All the meridians of longitude are numbered with reference to this prime or zero meridian. The meridians of the celestial sphere, the hour circles, are also measured with reference to a prime meridian, known as the prime hour circle.

The prime hour circle is that circle which passes through the "First Point Of Aries." This is a point located on the celestial equator and represents that point where the Sun, in its annual journey, passes from the southern half of the celestial sphere to the northern half. Aries is one of the constellations of the Zodiac and can be seen in Figure 28. As the Sun crosses this point, we note that the days are equal in length to the nights, and we say that the season of spring has begun — the vernal equinox.

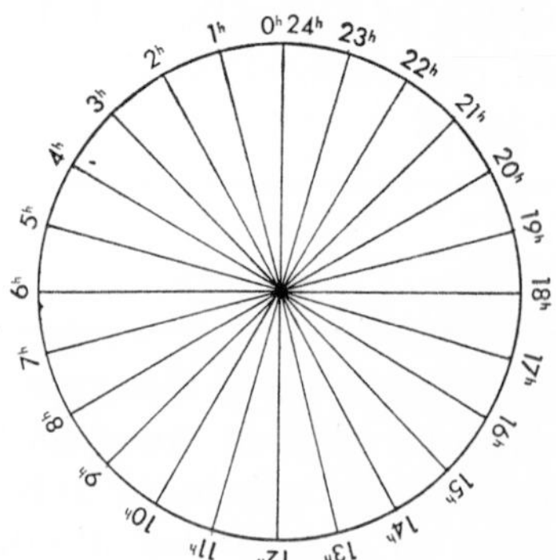

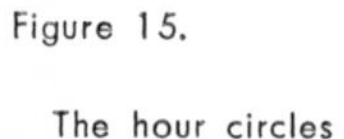
Figure 15.

The hour circles

To locate the position of a star along one of these great hour circles (we use the term *right ascension* to indicate this position), we count off the number of sidereal hours from the prime (zero hour) meridian. Sidereal time is the time that is based on the apparent movement of the stars, while the time notations used in daily life are based on the apparent movement of the Sun — solar time. The right ascension of a star is expressed as hours, minutes, and seconds, from 0 to 24 hours. Right ascension is measured eastward from the 0^h (zero hour) meridian.

Right ascension may also be expressed as degrees (from 0° to 360°) although it is more usually indicated as sidereal hour angles (from 0° to 24°). These two notations can be easily converted, one to the other, by using the following relationship:

$$1 \text{ hour} = 15^\circ, \quad 1^\circ = 4 \text{ minutes}$$

With the position of the star denoted by its right ascension (R.A.) and its declination (Dec.), the observer has only to turn his telescope to that point in the sky in order to find what he is seeking. Perhaps an illustration will show how an actual star position may be plotted.

Let us suppose that the observer wishes to find Capella. Actually, Capella is one of the brightest stars in the northern sky and is a familiar landmark for all observers. However, for the sake of illustration, the position of Cappella will be plotted. On referring to a star catalogue or star atlas, the following notation will be found:

	R. A.	Dec.
Capella	$5^h\ 12^m$	+45° 58′

Remembering that we have mentally superimposed a gigantic grid of lines on the celestial sphere, we plot the R.A. of Capella at 5 hours and 12 minutes and the Dec. at 45 degrees and 58 minutes. (The + in front of the declination figure indicates that it is north of the celestial equator. Declinations south are preceeded by a minus symbol).

In order to plot the star position on the chart shown in Figure 16, it will be necessary to convert the R.A. from sidereal hour angles to degrees, as the divisions in the polar gridwork shown are marked off in degrees. The following calculation accomplishes this conversion:

R.A. Capella : $5^h\ 12^m$
(1hour = 15°)
5 hours = $15° \times 5 = 75°$
(1 degree = 4 minutes)
12 minutes/4 = 3°

Therefore, the R.A. of Cappella in degrees is equal to :

$$75° + 3° = 78°$$

Referring to the polar grid chart of Figure 16, the position of Capella is fixed at the point where the two coordinates meet; at R.A. = 78° and Dec. = 46° (approximately). Star charts will also show that Capella is a star in the constellation Auriga.

The field of view of the telescope may be used as a means of measuring the distance between specific points in the heavens. The size of the field of any telescope-eyepiece combination may be determined by seeing how long it takes for a star to drift across the telescope's field.

Stars (near the celestial equator) appear to move from east to west at the rate of about 1° in four minutes. To determine the field of the telescope, it is necessary, merely, to time the drift of a star across the field. Then divide the time, in minutes, by four to obtain the size of the field in degrees. For instance, it may take a star five minutes and thirty seconds to cross the field. The field, therefore, measures:

$$\frac{5.5 \text{ minutes}}{4} = 1.4° \text{ approximately}$$

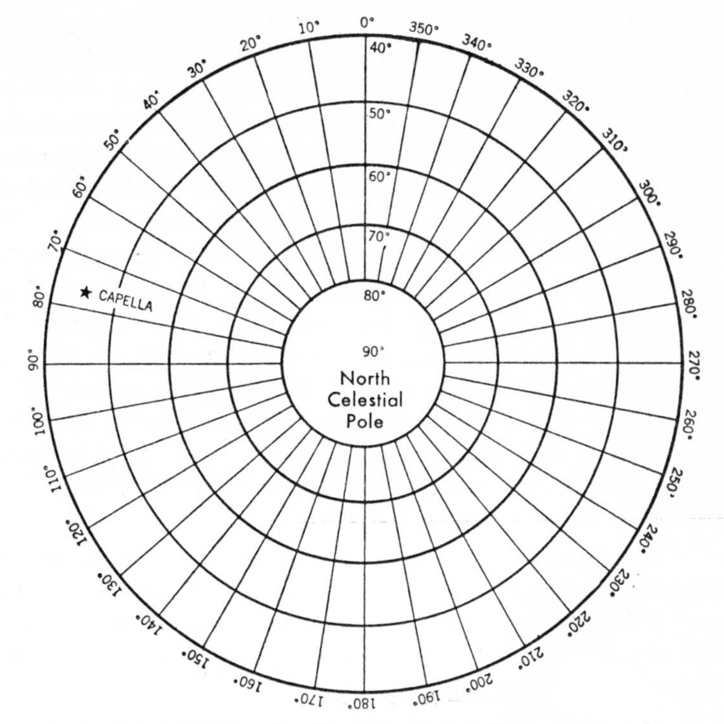

Figure 16. Plotting a star's position

This information is useful as the number of degrees between certain stars may be obtained from star charts or catalogues. Knowing the size of the field, the distance may be "stepped off" by shifting the telescope the proper number of field widths. For example, two stars are separated by 8.5°. Using the field calculated above, six field widths of the telescope, stepped off, one by one, will bring the observer from one star to the other.

$$6 \times 1.4^\circ = 8.5^\circ \text{ approximately}$$

Once the sky-watcher understands the method of locating a star by grid coordinates, it becomes clear that the equatorial telescope mount has some decided advantages. It enables the observer to use the listed coordinates of an object's position in the sky to bring it quickly into the field of view. While this is the one great advantage of the equatorial mount over the altazimuth, it must be noted that very careful and precise adjustment of the equatorial is required before sky objects can be located in this manner. This involves the use of "setting circles" which are discussed later in this chapter.

The equatorial mount consists of two axes at right angles to each other. The telescope, in its cradle, is free to move about either of the two axes. See Figure 17. The main task in setting up an equatorial is to line up the polar axis with the axis of the celestial sphere. For ordinary work the polar axis may be lined up by pointing the telescope at Polaris — the Pole star — so called because its position is very close to the North Celestial Pole.

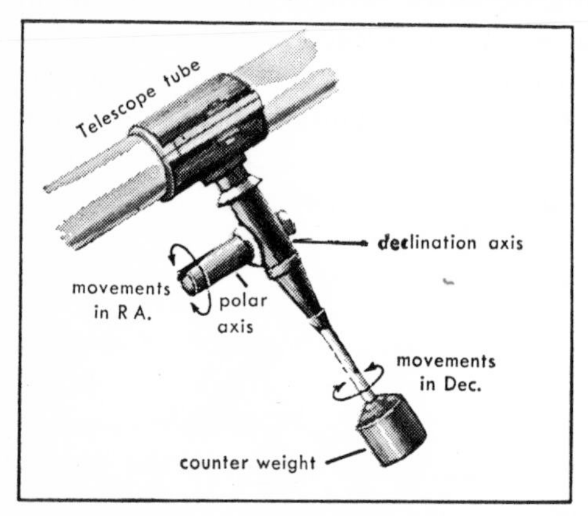

Figure 17.

The equatorial mount

Recalling the star trails in the photograph on page 135, it will be noted that the apparent motion of the stars is in great circles around the Pole — which we mark by the position of Polaris. To follow a star with an equatorial mount, therefore, the telescope need only be rotated about the polar axis. This movement will sweep out a circle, as the observer follows a star, that parallels the circular lines of declination. This is a movement in right ascension and follows the star around the celestial pole.

The declination axis rotates around the polar axis and, simply speaking, controls the up and down movements of the telescope. After locating a star, the declination axis may be clamped and the star is then followed by movements around the polar axis only. Most equatorial mounts are fitted with slow motions that allow the sky-watcher to track a star smoothly and accurately.

Setting Circles and Clock Drives

Some equatorial mounts are equipped with setting circles. The task of finding some of the less familiar sky objects is greatly eased if setting circles are used with a properly adjusted equatorial mount. Setting circles are graduated metal or plastic discs which are mounted on the shafts of the two axes of the telescope mounting. The declination circle is graduated in degrees of angle and the hour circle for right ascension is graduated in hours from 0^h to 24^h. Many setting circles are fitted with vernier scales to permit accurate fractional readings. See Figure 18.

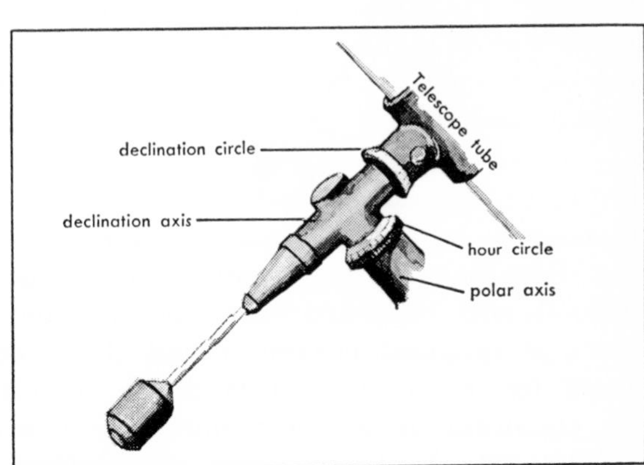

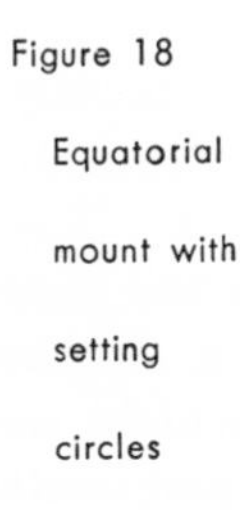
Figure 18 Equatorial mount with setting circles

There are several ways to use setting circles. The simplest method is to fix the telescope on a well known bright star in the vicinity of the object that is being sought.

Let us suppose that it is desired to find the "Great Nebula" in Andromeda. Star charts indicate that this object is located at R.A. = 0^h 40^m, and Dec. = + 41° 0′. Capella, in the constellation Auriga, is a bright star not too far away, and it is on Capella that the telescope is fixed. A simple calculation determines the distance of the "Great Nebula" from Capella.

Capella	5^h 12^m	+45° 58′
Great Nebula	0^h 40^m	+41° 0′

Subtract the values of the coordinates for the position of the object which is being sought from the coordinates of the object on which the telescope is fixed. This will give us, in the case above, the distance in right ascension of the nebula from Capella, as 4^h 32^m and in declination the distance is 4° 58′.

With Capella centered in the field of the telescope, the declination axis is clamped and the telescope is rotated around the polar axis until 4^h 32^m westward has been marked off on the setting circle. The polar axis is then clamped. Now, the declination axis is unclamped and the telescope is moved 4° 58′ southward. If the procedure has been carefully followed, the observer will find the "Great Nebula" in the field of his instrument.

In addition to setting circles, equatorial mounts may be fitted with clock drives, although it is somewhat unusual to find simple amateur equipment so fitted. The clock drive moves the telescope (by means of a motor and gears) around the polar axis at the same rate at which the star appears to travel. Thus, long time exposures in photography can be made without continuous adjustments of the telescope by the observer. Clock drives may be weight driven, spring wound, or operated by an electric motor. There are even attachments that will power a clock drive with an automobile battery.

At this point it may be well to add an explanatory

note. Many amateur astronomers derive great pleasure from their sky studies without ever using a setting circle or computing sidereal time. Just as it is perfectly possible to travel from Chicago to New Orleans without calculating changes in latitude and longitude, so is it possible for the amateur sky-watcher to find his way among the stars without using mathematics or precision instruments. Chapter V is designed to explain and illustrate some simpler methods of exploring the stars.

Among the basic equipment for any serious sky observer is a collection of star charts, catalogues, and atlases. These are the "road maps" that he must follow to locate objects of interest in the sky. Some simple star charts are included in the Appendix and in the insert on the back cover of this book and they will help the beginner to become oriented with the northern sky. As the observer gains in experience, he will feel the need for more detailed charts and listings of the heavenly bodies. Recommendations of some of the best sources of such information are to be found in Chapter V.

Telescope Adjustments

As a general rule, reflecting telescopes are more likely to be in need of adjustment than refractors. Proper alignment of the mirrors, both main and diagonal, are

Figure 19. Alignment of main mirror in a reflecting telescope

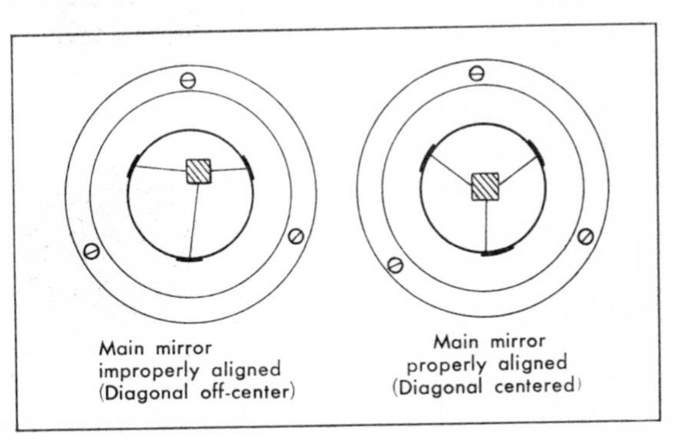

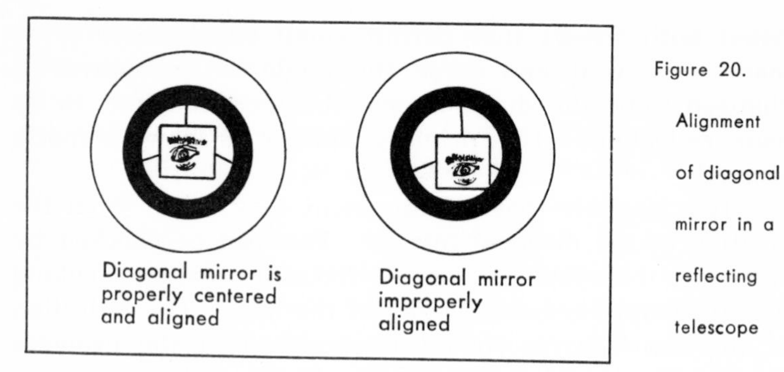

Figure 20. Alignment of diagonal mirror in a reflecting telescope

prerequisites to obtaining satisfactory, undistorted images. Most reflectors are so constructed that minor adjustments of the mirrors can easily be made.

To determine if the main mirror is properly aligned, the observer should look down the open end of the tube. It will be noted that the diagonal mirror is seen against the background of its magnified reflection from the main mirror. If the diagonal is not centered in its reflection, then the main mirror is probably out of alignment. See Figure 19.

The primary mirror mounting, or cell, is usually

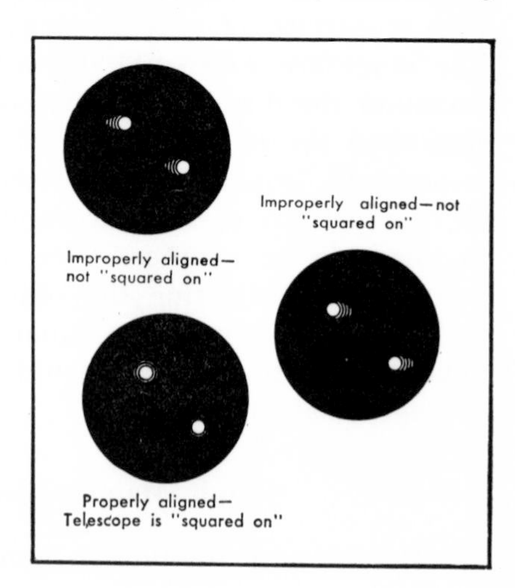

Figure 21. "Squaring on" the telescope

fitted with screws that permit small adjustments to be made. By trial and error the angle of the mirror is changed until the diagonal may be seen centered in its own reflection. The primary mirror is now properly aligned.

It is possible that misalignment may result from the position of the diagonal mirror. This can be checked by removing the eyepiece from its focusing tube and looking into the empty eyepiece holder of the tube. The reflection of the main mirror should be centered in the eyepiece tube as illustrated in Figure 20. If the reflection is not in line, the diagonal mirror should be adjusted on its mountings to bring about the proper alignment.

One of the big advantages of the refractor is that it rarely develops alignment problems. The sky-watcher can check the alignment of his refractor by the following procedure: Using an eyepiece of high magnification (150 X or greater), focus the telescope on a fairly bright star. Then put the telescope slightly out of focus and examine the quality of the image. If the objective lens is properly aligned at right angles to the axis of the entering light rays, then the image will appear as a tiny disc of light with a pattern of several rings or halos surrounding it. The rings are part of a diffraction pattern and if they surround the disc of light without displacement to either side, then the objective lens is aligned and the telescope is properly "squared on". If the telescope is not squared on, the pattern of the surrounding rings will be shifted to one side or another. See Figure 21. This can be corrected by adjusting the objective lens mount so that the telescope is properly squared on. It is a somewhat delicate adjustment and should not be attempted by the average amateur.

Simple Maintenance Procedures

Proper and intelligent handling of equipment will

prevent the occurrence of many annoying problems. Telescopes are precision mechanical and optical instruments and should be handled with care and respect. The instrument should be stored in its case and protected from dust when not in use. In setting up the telescope, avoid jarring it or handling it carelessly. Preventive maintenance is the best guarantee against future difficulty.

Mirrors and lenses are the heart of the telescope's structure. Special care must be taken to protect the optical elements from damage. Dust caps of cloth or plastic should be placed over lenses and mirrors whenever the telescope is stored for any period of time. If dust is found on the optical surfaces, a soft camel's-hair brush should be used to gently sweep it away. Such a brush can be purchased at a hobby shop or art store and should be stored in the telescope case. Never rub an optical surface without first dusting it thoroughly, as a tiny particle of dirt or grit on a cloth can gouge and scratch a lens or mirror badly. Always brush away dust with a soft-bristled brush.

When lenses or mirrors need cleaning beyond what can be accomplished with a lens brush, the wise amateur proceeds with caution. A cleaning solution, no stronger than mild soap and water, in combination with a soft, lint-free cloth should be gently applied to the optical surface without rubbing. A thorough rinse in clear water should follow and the optical element is not rubbed dry but allowed, instead, to air dry.

The use of solvents such as xylene and alcohol for cleaning purposes is not recommended. Many objective lenses are made of several elements cemented together and the aforementioned solvents could possibly dissolve the bonding cement.

Eyepieces should be cared for and cleaned like any other optical element. Unfortunately, eyepieces are constructed so that they can be taken apart. The amateur should not attempt this because the lenses of the eyepiece are carefully aligned during manufacture and careless handling could lead to unfortunate mishaps. Store eyepieces in dustproof containers and protect them from shock.

Another maintenance problem, peculiar to reflectors, involves the metallic coating of the mirror. With normal exposure and use, the silver or aluminum coating will eventually wear away. Re-coating is a job for the professional, not for the amateur. Experience has shown that aluminizing produces longer wearing coatings than the older silvering process.

Conditions For Observing

At times the factors that make for good viewing have nothing to do with the optics of the telescope. Atmospheric conditions determine, more often than most people realize, how successful the sky-watcher will be. You may have a magnificent telescope on a rock-steady mounting, but when the blanket of air surrounding the earth is shifting and turbulent, the instrument may as well be left in its case.

The Earth's atmosphere is rarely still. The motion of air currents affects our vision even without the magnifying effects of the telescope. Everyone is aware of the optical distortions caused by the rippling and waverings of air currents above a heated surface. On some nights this can cause telescope images to dance and "boil" until the sky-watcher is forced to abandon his attempts at observation. This effect is more of a problem when the objects to be viewed are near the horizon, for it is here that the Earth's blanketing atmosphere is thickest. Observations made at the zenith are less affected by atmospheric instability. This problem is intensified in reflecting telescopes as air currents within the open tube merely compound the viewing difficulty.

Two other distractions that can plague the sky-watcher, are clouds and interfering light. A bank of clouds can roll in with astonishing speed to cover the sky and put an end to observing for the night. A heavy haze will usually prevent good telescope viewing, but a faint haze is often characteristic of a still atmosphere and good "seeing" may be possible.

City lights may make it very difficult to carry out effective observations. Even in suburban backyards the viewer should set up his instrument so that there is no interference from nearby house lights.

Moonlight is another factor that must be reckoned with. A full moon can dim nearby stars and planets and, in general, curtail sky-watching. The Moon itself, under these conditions, is a poor subject for viewing.

When these interruptions occur, the amateur can spend his time in worthwhile fashion by checking through his star atlas, memorizing constellation boundaries, and planning new observation programs. The wonders of the sky are worth waiting for.

CHAPTER III

THE EARTH'S NEIGHBORS IN SPACE

Then felt I like some watcher of the skies
When a new planet swims into his ken.

John Keats

III. THE EARTH'S NEIGHBORS IN SPACE

Our Satellite: The Moon

THE MOON, the celestial body nearest to the Earth, well deserves its popularity among amateur astronomers as a favorite object of study. Revolving around our planet at the relatively close distance of 238,000 miles (average distance), our single satellite reveals fascinating surface details to the observer equipped with a small telescope or even with binoculars, while to the naked eye sufficient markings are visible to allow imaginative people to see a Man in the Moon.

Our satellite is a bare, airless, rocky sphere; it will afford little welcome to any space traveler who sets foot upon it. The landscape, or, properly speaking, moonscape, is a weird aggregation of deep craters, craggy mountain ranges, dry "seas", and looming cliffs. Plant or animal life on such an inhospitable surface is most unlikely, and all evidence indicates that nothing lives upon the Moon.

The diameter of the Moon is some 2,160 miles, and it takes about 27 days for it to make one complete revolution around the Earth. Curiously enough, the Moon is rotating on its own axis at the same rate at which it orbits the Earth. Thus, our satellite always presents the same face to us, and the "other side" of the Moon has never actually been seen by man, except for photographs made by space satellites. However, we really see almost 60% of the Moon's surface due to a rocking or wobbling on its axis because of variations in orbital speed. These wobbles, known as librations, permit us to glimpse, for periods of time, some of the dark side of the Moon. It seems to be much like the hemisphere that faces us.

Moonlight, of course, is really the light of the Sun being reflected from the surface of the Moon which acts as a kind of dull mirror in space. Lacking a protective atmosphere, the lighted face of the moon is fiercely heated by the Sun's rays and temperatures result that are hot enough to boil water (which is absent on the Moon) — about 250 degrees Fahrenheit. When the Sun's rays no longer fall on the Moon's surface, the temperature drops to a frigid 110 degrees below zero.

The shape of the Moon appears to undergo a gradual nightly change as we observe it from the Earth. These apparent changes in the Moon's shape result from the fact that as the lunar sphere circles the Earth, an observer sees different portions of the illuminated hemisphere, depending on the Moon's position in its orbit. Each of these illuminated visible segments is given a name and represents one of the phases of the Moon. Figure 22 diagrams the Moon's phases and it can be seen why they appear to us as they do.

Considering that the Moon is almost a quarter of a million miles away, we know a good deal about its surface. It has been mapped, photographed, and charted better, perhaps, than some parts of our own planet. Virtually every crater, crevasse, cliff, and contour has been given a name, usually that of a famed scientist or philosopher. There are nearly 700 named craters. The map shown in Figure 23 merely indicates some of the more important landmarks that can be readily seen on the lunar surface. More detailed maps are available and the interested observer should obtain a large scale map of the Moon. Sketch maps and drawings of the Moon made by the observer will help him to become familiar with the curious features of the lunar landscape.

The Moon is best observed before and after the new moon phase. In crescent phase there is little glare and the "sidelighting" causes long shadows which add depth

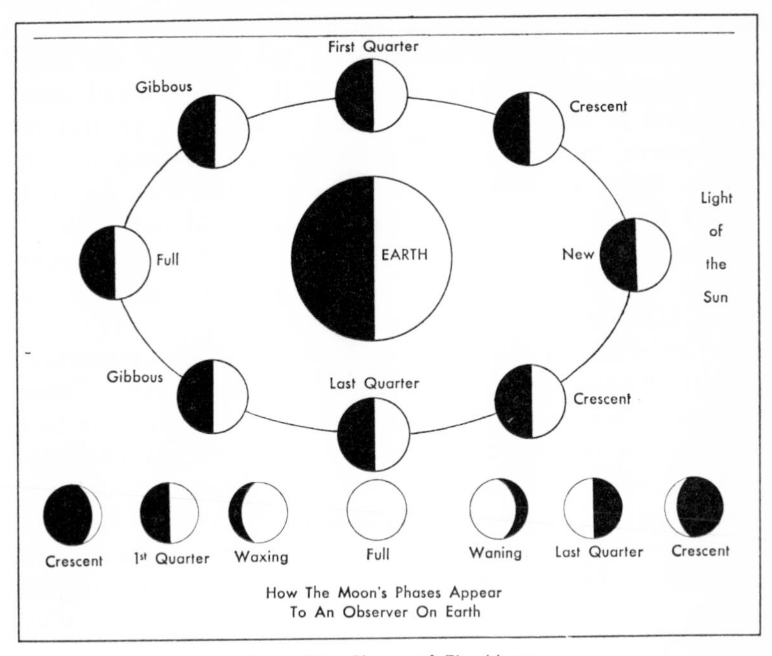

Figure 22. Phases of The Moon

and clarity to the Moon's landscape. As the Moon approaches the quarter phases the glare of the reflected sunlight increases, making effective viewing more difficult. At such times a lunar filter attached to the telescope eyepiece cuts down excess light and increases the contrast. This useful accessory permits making detailed observations in spite of less favorable viewing conditions.

The line of demarcation between the dark area and the sunlit area of the Moon is called the "terminator". It is at, or near, the terminator that the Moon's surface can be best observed. The alert observer can see some truly spectacular lunar phenomena by training his telescope in the area of the terminator. Sudden glints of sunlight glancing off a mountain peak while the rest of the landscape is in shadow provide a starting glimpse into the true nature of the lunar scene.

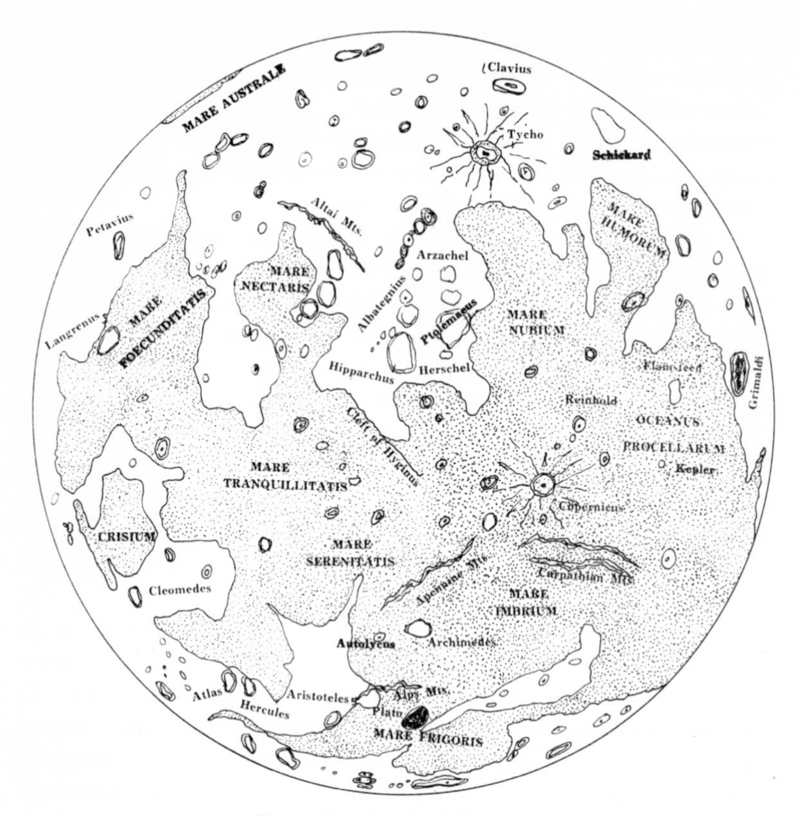

Figure 23. Sketch of The Moon

On occasion, the Moon passes between the observer and a star or planet, hiding the object from view. This is known as an "occultation" and is extremely interesting to watch in the field of the telescope. When the Moon occults a star it provides evidence that there is no lunar atmosphere. In the telescope the observer will be able to see the star drift slowly across to the Moon's edge, and in the instant of passing behind the Moon, it will disappear instantly like a snuffed candle. There is no flickering or winking because the Moon has no atmosphere to distort the light rays emanating from the star.

The Moon's occultations can be predicted in advance and the various astronomical almanacs will list the major occultations for the current year. The exact time of these occultations is used in determining distances and in mapmaking. Many amateurs enjoy timing these lunar phenomena and reporting the results.

During an eclipse of the Moon, the observer will be fascinated by the strange color changes that transform the familiar features of the Moon's disc. The Moon is eclipsed when it passes through the cone of shadow cast by the Earth. Eclipses occur only when Earth, Moon, and Sun all lie along the same line. See Figure 24.

The Moon does not disappear completely on entering the shadow cast by the Earth as its disc is illuminated by a faint, ruddy glow. This illumination comes from the rays of the Sun which are refracted (bent) by the atmosphere of the Earth and a beautiful coppery tint is imparted to the Moon's landscape.

As the Moon passes into the Earth's shadow, it is shielded from the Sun's rays and the consequent temperature drop is severe, probably as much as 100° F. Some observers feel that this sudden cooling may cause changes in the appearance of the Moon due to the heaving and cracking of the lunar crust. This could prove a fertile field for study by amateur astronomers.

Although the Moon has been studied for centuries, little is known about the formation of its characteristic

Figure 24. The Eclipse of The Moon

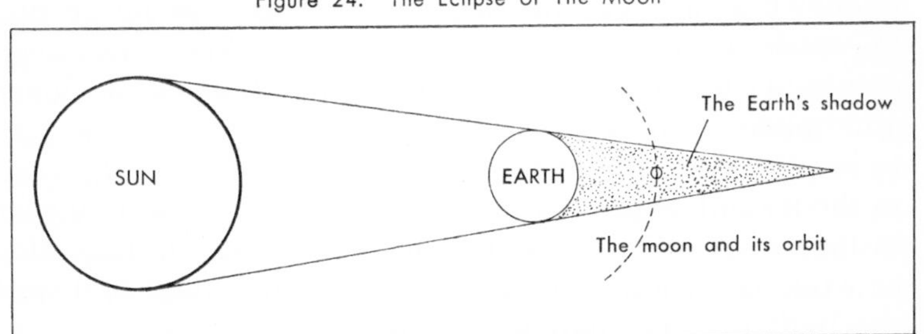

craters, valleys, and mountains. There are some very real objections to the theory that meteor bombardment is responsible for the scarred appearance of the lunar face. Theories suggesting volcanic action as a causal factor are not completely satisfactory either. There is still much to be learned about the Earth's closest neighbor in space.

Our Nearest Star: The Sun

93,000,000 miles from the Earth an enormous globe of glowing, incredibly hot gas pours its light and heat outward into space. This is a star — not a tiny point of light winking coldly against a blue velvet sky — but a roaring, blasting atomic furnace spewing forth fiery tongues of glaring vapors for a million miles above its surface. This is our Sun.

The sky-watcher who wishes to study our nearest star must use extreme caution. There is real danger in looking at the Sun's disc directly with the telescope.

For direct observation of the Sun, a Sun glass or Sun filter must be attached to the eyepiece in order to reduce the intensity of the Sun's rays. Such a filter is usually provided as a piece of auxiliary equipment with a telescope. The filter will reduce the intensity of the light but the heat of the Sun will still be strong. Strong enough, perhaps, to crack the filter and in that instant serious eye damage is possible.

An even safer method is to obtain a Sun diagonal. This is a device which employs a flat wedge of glass that permits the observer to make direct observations of the Sun with relative safety. The wedge of glass, known as a Herschel wedge, is a flat prism with an angle of about 10°. Such a prism, arranged much like a star diagonal, will only reflect about 5% of the Sun's light to the observer, while the rest passes harmlessly through the glass wedge. In this way, the potential hazard of direct observation may be eliminated. However, as a general rule, it is far safer to study the Sun by indirect projection techniques.

Projection of the Sun's image is a relatively simple matter. Some telescopes are equipped with a Sun projection screen which is an accessory that every observer will find useful. Figure 25 illustrates how the Sun projection screen may be used on a telescope equipped with a star diagonal.

The telescope is turned to point at the Sun by sighting along the tube through half-closed lids. An even safer method is to sight the telescope by looking at the Sun through a double thickness of overexposed and developed photographic film.

A piece of white cardboard is then held several inches from the eyepiece, and the telescope is adjusted until the image of the Sun's disc is thrown upon the card. The image may be focused by racking the eyepiece in or out, or by moving the card closer or farther from the eyepiece.

Figure 25.

Using The Sun Projection Screen

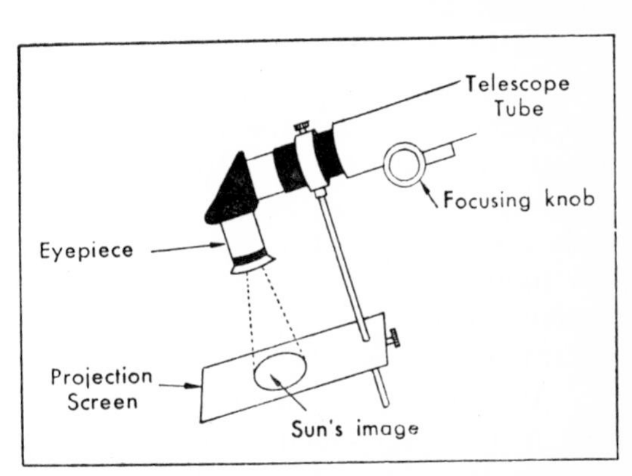

This method will demonstrate the solar phenomena as well as any other. It is particularly well adapted for demonstrating sunspots. Sunspots appear as dark areas on the face of the Sun. The photograph on page 71 is one of the finest that has been made of sunspot activity. The spots show the typically dark center area, the umbra, and a lighter colored rim, the penumbra.

Sunspots may be relatively small or they may be large

enough to extend over an area of almost 100,000 miles on the Sun's face. The spots are indications of deep turbulences within the Sun and they are often described as "tornados" or storms. Their true cause is unknown although it is believed likely that they are associated with atomic reactions on the Sun.

The appearance of the spots on the Sun's face can seriously affect magnetic phenomena on Earth. The magnetic storms on the Sun's disc can cause a compass needle to behave strangely — swinging from one compass point to another and making the instrument useless for navigational purposes. With the disruption of the Earth's magnetic field, radio communications suffer and, during severe outbreaks, international short-wave broadcasting may break down completely. Another indication of the magnetic nature of sunspots is the appearance of auroras in the Earth's atmosphere when sunspot activity is at a peak.

Considerable study has been made, especially during the recent Geophysical Year, of the magnetic storms that sweep across the face of the Sun, but there still remains much to be learned of these cyclical outbreaks that affect the Earth so strangely.

If sunspots are observed periodically and charted, it will be noted that they move steadily across the Sun's disc. A specific sunspot will travel over the face of the Sun in about two weeks. The movement, of course, is not the movement of the spot but of the entire Sun which is rotating on its axis.

The observation of the position and movement of sunspots is of prime importance. It will be found that some sunspots appear, remain in view for a few days, and disappear. Other sunspots may be observed as they make a complete journey across the face of the Sun. It should be remembered that the sunspot movement is actually due to the Sun's rotation. The sunspots will move across the

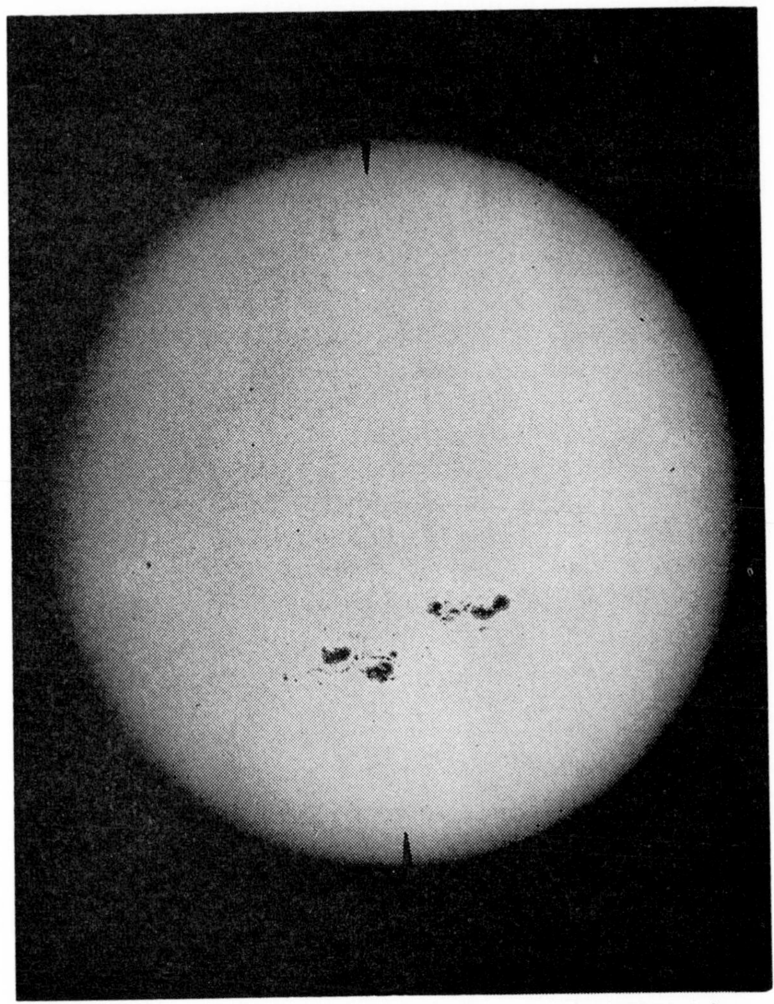

Photograph from the Mount Wilson and Palomar Observatories.

Photograph of the Sun showing large sunspots. Note dark center and lighter border of the spots.

face of the Sun in about fourteen days.

Sunspot activity varies considerably. In some years only a relatively few sunspots will be observed. At other times, more than 100 sunspots will be seen to appear in a single day. The activity of this solar phenomenon seems to be periodic or cyclical. Most authorities agree that there is a period of approximately eleven years between one burst of maximum activity to the next maximum.

One of the most magnificent sights to be seen by man is that of a solar prominence — a gigantic, leaping spear of flaming gas thrusting hundreds of thousands of miles above the surface of the Sun. Solar prominences cannot be seen normally without special equipment such as the spectrohelioscope and monochromatic filters. These are beyond the reach, both technically and economically, of the amateur astronomer. However, during the relatively rare periods of total solar eclipse this phenomenon and others may be glimpsed by the alert observer.

A solar eclipse occurs when the Moon passes between the Earth and the Sun. See Figure 26. The Moon's shadow travels in an arcing line over the Earth's surface and those in the path of that moving shadow will be fortunate enough to see what is really one of Nature's most awesome spectacles.

Observers on Earth who are in the dark cone of shadow called the umbra will be able to see a total eclipse

Figure 26. The Solar Eclipse

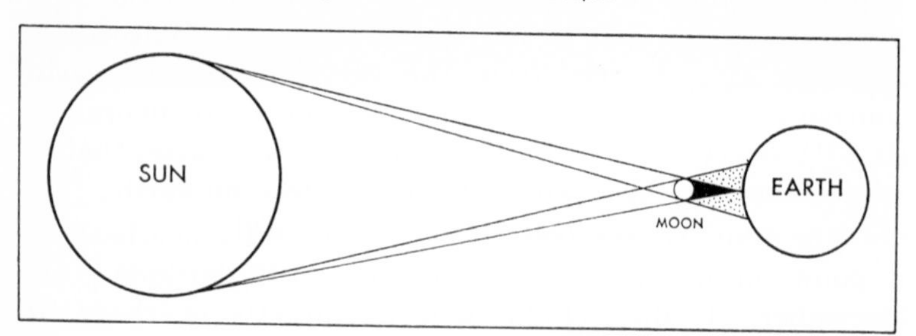

of the Sun. The half-shadowed region of the penumbra will sweep out a larger path, over the Earth's surface, than will the smaller umbra. Viewers in the region traversed by the penumbra will see only a partial eclipse.

During the few moments of totality, solar prominences may be seen as well as the corona — a glowing halo or crown of light surrounding the eclipsed solar disc. And in the instant that the Moon's departing shadow begins to unveil the face of the Sun, a brilliant flash of light, the "Diamond Ring," may be seen. Similar, but less intense, flashes of light may be observed during totality. These are known as "Baily's Beads."

Even during a total eclipse, the sky-watcher is cautioned to use all safeguards in observing the Sun. Solar filters must be attached to telescope eyepieces, for even the momentary flashes during totality could affect the eye with serious results.

The Zodiac: Path Of The Planets

The Sun and its planetary family travel across the sky in a well-worn path. The Sun's trail, which it follows year after year, is known as the "ecliptic." The apparent path of the Sun is traced against the background of the stars and as the Sun makes its yearly circle it moves about one degree each day along the ecliptic.

The position of the ecliptic, this avenue of the planets, appears to change in the sky as the earthly year progresses. This is due to the tilt of the earth's axis which is about 23½ degrees from the vertical. As the earth journeys about the Sun, the axis of the earth maintains its 23½ degree tilt. It is this axial tilt, of course, that is responsible for the change of seasons here on earth.

On June 21, the ecliptic will be directly overhead at a point on the earth 23½ degrees north latitude. On December 21, the ecliptic will be directly overhead at a point on the earth 23½ degrees south latitude. These dates, the solstices, mark the beginnings of the summer and winter seasons and represent opposite points on the orbit of the earth.

Orbiting around the Sun, the planetary group travels the same path, but in a broader band due to their angled orbits around the Sun. See Figure 27. This broad band (it actually spreads across a width of about 16°) is called

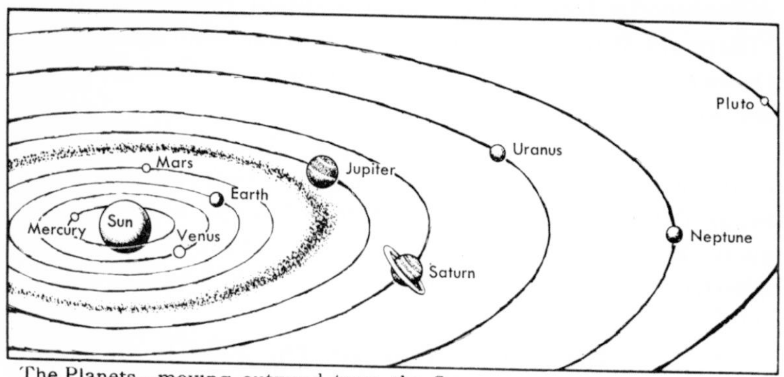

The Planets—moving outward from the Sun:
Mercury, Venus, Earth, Mars (The Belt of Asteroids), Jupiter, Saturn, Uranus, Neptune, Pluto

Figure 27. The Planets of The Solar System

the Zodiac. This is a word of Greek origin meaning "circle of animals," as the constellations which lie in the area of the Zodiac are mostly those actually named for animals. See Figure 28.

The twelve Zodiacal constellations are referred to as the "signs of the Zodiac." Astronomical publications periodically list the positions of the planets with their respective locations in the band of the Zodiac. The signs of the Zodiac and their symbols are shown on page 76.

Planets are located in the sky by their relative positions against the background of the Zodiacal constellations as seen by an observer on Earth. A specific planet is said to be "in" the Zodiacal constellation that forms its background, as seen from the Earth. Thus, in Figure 29,

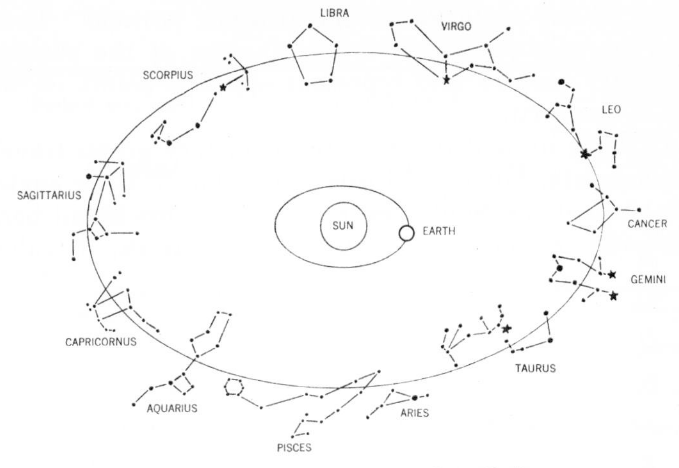

Figure 28. The Constellations of the Zodiac

Saturn is in Virgo, Jupiter is in Sagittarius, Mars is in Gemini. The Sun, in the diagram, is "in" Leo.

A table of planet locations is listed in the Appendix. Reference should be made to astronomical almanacs and periodicals for further information. The *American*

Figure 29. Planetary Positions In The Zodiac

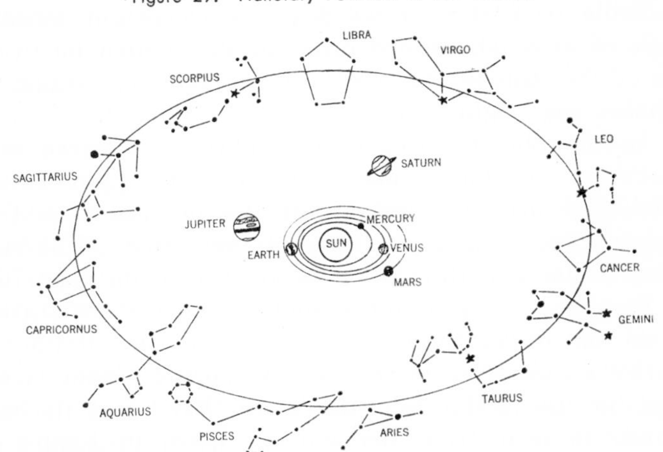

SIGNS OF THE ZODIAC

Symbol	Constellation	Date Sun Enters
♈	Aries—The Ram	March 21
♉	Taurus—The Bull	April 20
♊	Gemini—The Twins	May 21
♋	Cancer—The Crab	June 22
♌	Leo—The Lion	July 23
♍	Virgo—The Virgin	August 23
♎	Libra—The Scales	September 23
♏	Scorpio—The Scorpion	October 24
♐	Sagittarius—The Archer	November 22
♑	Capricornus—The Goat	December 22
♒	Aquarius—The Water Bearer	January 20
♓	Pisces—The Fishes	February 19

Ephemeris and Nautical Almanac, an annual publication obtainable from the United States Government Printing Office, contains all needed information on planetary positions. A monthly publication, *Sky and Telescope* magazine, publishes such data in each issue for the current month.

As the planets circle the Sun, their positions with respect to the Earth are constantly changing. These positions or aspects have specific names and should be learned. The planets are usually classified as *inferior* planets — those with orbits between that of the Earth and the Sun, and as *superior* planets — those with orbits outside that of the Earth.

In the case of an inferior planet, such as Venus, when the planet lies in the same line as the Earth and the Sun, it is said to be in "conjunction." Figure 30 illustrates the

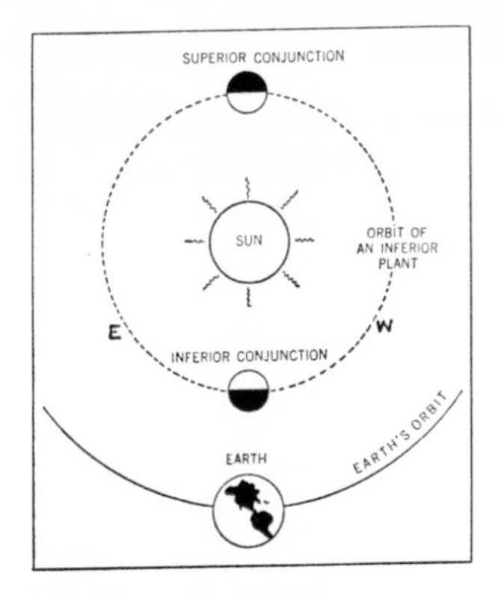

Figure 30. Aspects of an Inferior Planet

aspects of conjunction: superior conjunction when the planet is farthest from the Earth, and inferior conjunction when the planet lies closest to the Earth. It will be seen from the diagram that the planet shows phases as does the Moon. This is characteristic of an inferior planet. When the planet is in the position marked "W" it is said to be in greatest western "elongation"; at point "E" it is in greatest eastern "elongation."

The superior planets can lie in aspects of conjunction, opposition, or quadrature. It is of particular importance for the observer to know when the planet is in opposition; it is then that the planet is closest to the Earth and is best observed. Figure 31 indicates the aspects of a superior

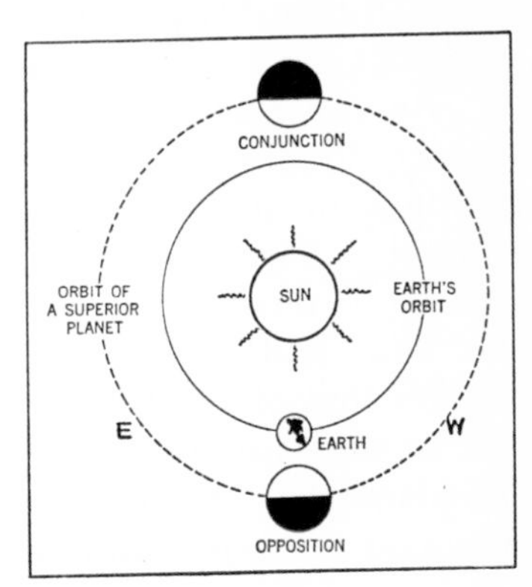

Figure 31. Aspects of a Superior Planet

planet such as Jupiter. When the planet lies at points "E" and "W" it is in eastern and western quadrature, respectively. It can be readily seen from the diagram that at opposition a superior planet is closest to the Earth and is best illuminated for effective observation.

The Inferior Planets

Mercury, the smallest planet (only half again the size of the Moon) completes its orbit around the Sun in only 88 days. This 88 day "year" is the shortest among the planets. The length of the "day" on Mercury, however, is the longest among the planets for it is eternal. Mercury always turns the same toward the Sun. The tiny planet rotates on its own axis at the same rate at which it revolves around the Sun.

This phenomenon is responsible for the fantastic temperature extremes on the planet. The "day" side is roasted by the Sun and temperatures are high enough to liquefy lead, about 700° F. The "night" side, where the Sun never shines, is cold — as cold as any object in the incredibly frigid depths of outer space.

Mercury is a difficult planet to observe in the telescope and when it is seen, the results, more often than not, are disappointing. It will appear as a small disc which, unfortunately, lies near the Sun where the glare renders it difficult to see. It is never more than 28 degrees from the Sun.

Late evening or early morning, after the Sun has set or before it has risen, is the best time for observation of Mercury. It is wise to consult published planetary data for information as to where Mercury may be seen. The best time to look for the planet is immediately after the Sun has set, when it is relatively high in the sky. Actually, it is never very high in the sky and observations are usually hindered by houses, trees and other objects that may obscure the horizon. The story is told that Copernicus never saw Mercury because of the evening and morning mists that rose from the river near his home.

Venus may be thought of as Earth's sister planet. It is very nearly the same size and its period of revolution around the Sun is more nearly that of Earth's than any other planet.

It is relatively easy to find Venus and observe it with a telescope but the observer should be warned that the view is far from spectacular. The planet appears as a bright, shining disc with virtually no visible surface details or markings.

As a matter of fact, the observer is not looking at the surface of the planet at all but, rather, at a dense blanket of clouds that always veil the planet. Even the "clouds" are not clouds as we know them in the Earth's atmosphere. Their true composition is unknown, some observers suggesting that they are immense clouds of white dust from the Venusian landscape below, while others feel that they are masses of carbon dioxide and water vapor.

The incredible voyage of the satellite Mariner II has shed a little new light on the theories held about the planet Venus. Passing within 22,000 miles of the planet, the satellite was able to make certain accurate radio observations. Basically, these observations revealed that the high temperatures previously recorded from Venus emanated from its surface rather than from its atmosphere and that the surface itself was somewhat smoother than the Moon.

The all-enveloping blanket of cloud still shrouds our sister planet in a veil of mystery. More satellite probes will be needed before scientists can determine if the surface of Venus is an arid, dusty desert or a supertropical humid jungle.

It is always more exciting to turn one's telescope on the outer planets, the superior planets. Surface markings are more distinct and observations are more interesting and have greater value.

The Superior Planets

Of the outer planets, none has a greater appeal for the average man than the planet Mars. So much has been written about the "red planet" that it is sometimes difficult to separate fact from fiction. Observers often fail to agree on what they see on the planet's surface and controversies rage on the interpretation of what they actually do see.

Useful observation of surface details on Mars is limited to those periods when the Earth and Mars come to opposition. Owing to the difference in size of their orbits and the rate of travel of the planets, they will only come to opposition at intervals of 780 days. Thus, good conditions for viewing occur only once in every two year period. Planetary oppositions are shown in the diagram of Figure 32. It may be seen that the opposition of 1956 was a very close one and that in 1971, the opposition will be equally as favorable. The numbers, in the diagram, between the planets represent the distance, in millions of miles, that separates the planets at opposition.

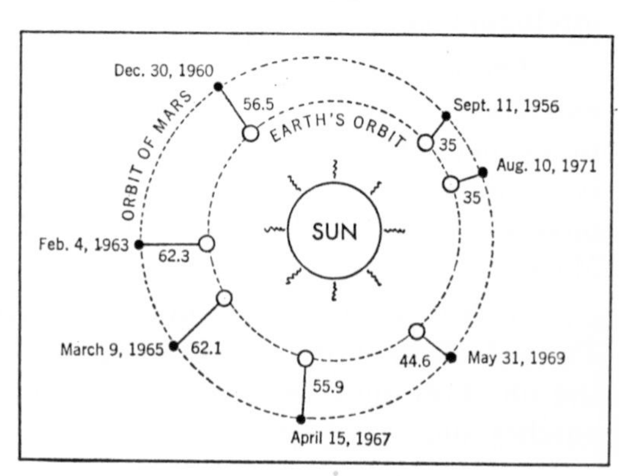

Figure 32.
The Oppositions
of Earth and Mars

On first viewing the planet, the sky-watcher is struck by two features: the general reddish coloration and the glistening white polar caps. Large areas of the planet will display a ruddy color splotched with darker, greenish patches. Some observers feel that the green areas are some sort of vegetation, possibly simple algal forms. This view is supported by observations that these areas seem to darken and increase in size during the Martian summer. The reddish areas are often considered to be "deserts", covered with a coppery dust.

The polar caps are icy or frosty deposits and are construed as evidence of the presence of water on Mars. These formations show the effect of the seasons by shrinking in size with the advent of the Martian summer. The release of water probably accounts for the "greening up" of the vegetation which occurs at the same time.

No discussion of Mars is complete without some mention of the famous "canals." Do they exist? The idea of the Martian canals derives from the work of an Italian astronomer, G.V. Schiaparelli, whose map of the planet, drawn in 1877, showed many thin, artificial-looking lines traversing the face of the planet. He called these lines, "canali", which really means "channels." Considerable excitement was engendered by Schiaparelli's "discovery." If canals existed, were they not constructed by intelligent beings on the planet?

There is little agreement among observers on the existence of the canals. Some reliable astronomers profess to see the fine markings; others insist they are not visible. It is, perhaps, significant that no satisfactory photographs have ever been made that show the presence of canals on Mars.

A drawing of the planet Mars appears in Figure 33. The polar cap on the side of the planet that is tilted toward the observer may be seen, as well as some of the darker patches of "vegetation." It is a worthwhile project for the amateur observer to make sketches and drawings of the objects he encounters in his solar system observations.

Unfortunately for the amateur sky-watcher, Mars is a small planet, only about half the size of the Earth. A small telescope, therefore, reveals little more than the gleaming, white polar caps. A three-inch refractor will also show, under good conditions, some of the surface markings. However, for detailed work, at least a six-inch refractor is needed.

Beyond Mars, space extends for 300 million miles before Jupiter's orbit is reached. This abyss of space is not empty, however, for this is the zone of the asteroids. These minor planets circle the Sun in a variety of orbits and the alert observer will be able to see some of the larger ones.

About 2,000 of these planetoids have been charted and named. The largest is Ceres, a stony mass about 500 miles in diameter. They range in size from this "giant" to others that are less than a mile across.

Asteroids are so small that they appear in the telescope as points of light, like a star, rather than as a planetary disc. As a result, the inexperienced observer may possibly confuse an asteroid with a "nova" or new star. Careful plotting of its position with respect to neighboring stars

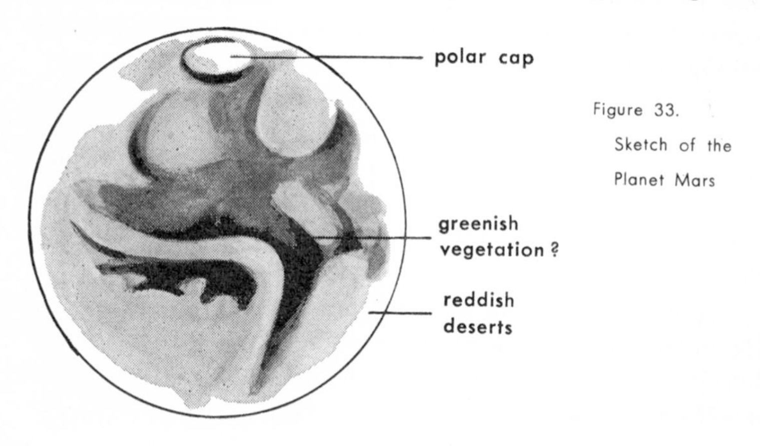

Figure 33. Sketch of the Planet Mars

will verify or disprove this. The nova will remain stationary, but the planetoid will shift its position from night to night.

Some of the major asteroid positions are listed in the various star almanacs such as the *American Ephemeris.* The sky-watcher will enjoy spotting one of these tiny space wanderers.

The largest body in our solar system, the giant planet Jupiter, is truly a magnificent object for observation. A small telescope or even good binoculars will reveal surface markings, and the four largest of Jupiter's twelve moons can easily be seen.

The planet itself is probably an ice-covered sphere of rock, the ice layer being about 15,000 miles thick. This frigid globe is wreathed in an atmosphere of poisonous gases, vapors of methane and ammonia. The temperature of this desolate world hovers at around 200° F. below zero. In view of the foregoing, it is felt that life on this planet is most improbable.

Some recent theories suggest that Jupiter is composed principally of hydrogen which achieves incredible densities in the interior of the planet. It should be noted that the actual composition of many of the celestial bodies is not completely known.

In the telescope, Jupiter appears as a large bright disc displaying a series of horizontal bands which are, actually, characteristics of the planet's atmosphere. These markings appear as dark and light zones of color, principally bands of brown, tan, and yellow. Especially interesting is the Great Red Spot — a nebulous, elliptical patch forming part of the planet's gaseous atmosphere. Within the past 80 years this huge reddish blotch, which once measured over 20,000 miles long, has been fading away and no satisfactory explanation has been offered for either its presence or its waning.

The four largest of Jupiter's moons are the only ones that have been named: Io, Europa, Ganymede, and Callisto.

They are readily observable as telescope objects. More often than not they will appear in a straight line as they orbit in virtually the same plane as Jupiter's equator. All four are not always seen as they may be passing behind the planet, crossing in front of it, or being eclipsed by it. Moons passing behind the planet are, of course, being occulted. In the second case, when a smaller celestial object passes in front of the face of a larger one, a "transit" is said to occur.

It is particularly striking to watch a transit of one of Jupiter's satellites across the planet. Actually, the passage of the satellite's dark shadow is more readily seen than the passage of the moon itself. See Figure 34.

In the diagram shown, satellite Number 1 is about to transit the face of Jupiter. Its shadow, Number 1A, has already begun a shadow transit. Moon Number 2 is occulted or hidden behind the plant. Satellite Number 3 is in the shadow cast by the giant planet and is thus in eclipse. Moon Number 4 is whirling around the planet in its orbit without special position at the moment. All of the positions of the planet and its satellites are, of course,

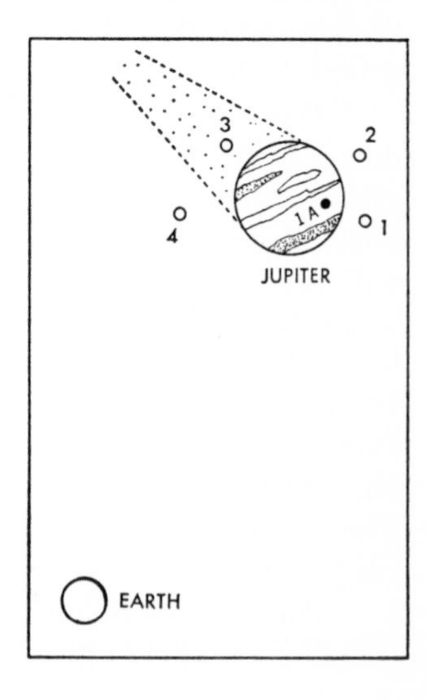

Figure 34.

Positions of

Jupiter's Moons

with respect to an observer on the planet Earth. Periodic observations of Jupiter and its four readily visible moons will, in the course of time, permit the careful observer to see all of the satellite positions as they circle their mother planet.

Standard celestial almanacs, such as the *American Ephemeris* and the *British Astronomical Association Handbook*, will not only give the position of Jupiter, but will list the occultations and transits of its moons as well.

Orbiting at a distance of 886,000,000 miles from the Sun, Saturn is the showpiece of the solar system. Among the planets, Saturn is second in size only to its huge neighbor, Jupiter; it is probably of similar composition. It has nine moons compared with Jupiter's twelve and its banded atmosphere is less prominent. Its famous ring system, however, makes Saturn one of the most spectacular of telescope objects.

The rings encircle the planet like a flattened disc and are probably made up of numberless particles of ice, rock, and gravel. The rings extend outward from the planet for about 50,000 miles on each side. The whole system is remarkably thin for its diameter. It is, probably, considerably less than 50 miles thick.

Even a small telescope will show Saturn as a golden disc enclosed within the cleanly marked, shining ring system. Galileo, using his very primitive telescope, was able to see the ring system of Saturn. Larger instruments will reveal considerable detail in the encircling ring. The separation between the center and outer ring, the dark band known as Cassini's Division, should be visible. Under good viewing conditions, the innermost "crepe" ring will appear as a dark, hazy structure. The "middle" ring will seem to shine more brightly than the other two. The diagram of Figure 35 illustrates the structure of the ring system.

The success of any observation of Saturn will depend, in part, on the angle at which the rings are viewed. If

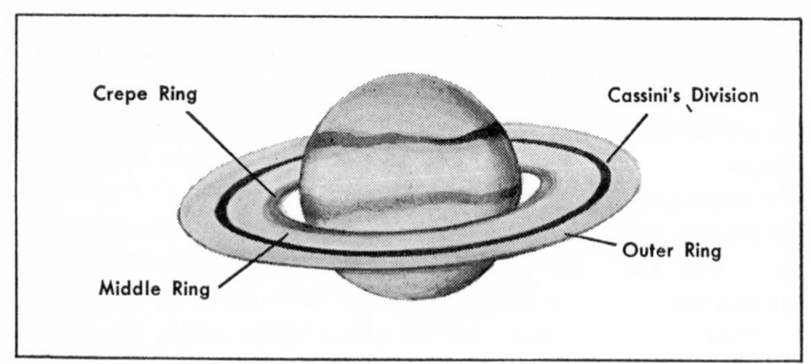

Figure 35. The Ring System of Saturn

they are edge-on to the Earth, the display is disappointing as the rings appear only as a relatively fine line. The various positions that the rings can assume are shown in Figure 36.

The farthest planets, of which only Uranus can be normally seen with the naked eye, are of little interest to the average observer. They are so far from Earth that even the best and most powerful amateur telescopes will fail to reveal any surface detail. Of course, there is a certain satisfaction in picking up Uranus or Neptune in the telescope's field, and the different publications, among them the *American Ephemeris*, will furnish the data to guide the interested observer to their locations in the sky.

Uranus, orbiting the Sun at a distance of about one and a half billion miles from Earth, can be seen in the

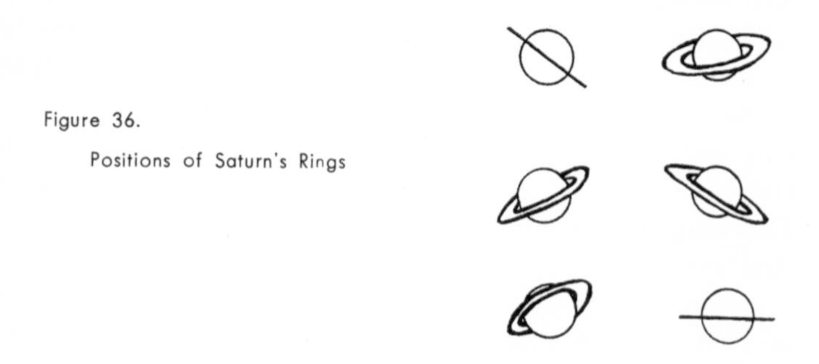

Figure 36.

Positions of Saturn's Rings

telescope without too much difficulty. Its appearance is that of a faint, greenish disc. Although Uranus has five satellites, none can be seen in the average telescope.

Neptune, a billion miles beyond Uranus, appears as a mere point of light in telescopes of moderate size. Only by checking its position from one night to the next can it be identified as a planet — a wanderer in the skies.

Neptune, curiously enough, was "discovered" by mathematical computation rather than by telescope observation. Astronomers noted that the orbit of Uranus varied more than it theoretically should. The suggestion was made that perhaps another planet, beyond Uranus, was exerting gravitational forces that were disrupting its normal orbit.

The orbit of such a hypothetical planet was calculated and when astronomers searched the area where the planet should be, their telescopes revealed the newly found member of the Sun's family in the exact predicted position.

Finally, tiny Pluto with its strange orbit and puzzling behavior was found, to complete the roster of the planets of our solar system. Many explanations have been offered for Pluto's small size as compared to its giant neighbors. It is believed likely that it was, at one time, one of Neptune's moons which broke away to travel along its own orbit in space.

Pluto is not visible except in the larger telescopes. However, there are wonders enough within the solar system to satisfy the most eager sky-watcher. Careful and patient observation is the key to success in planetary studies.

A table of planetary data is included in the Appendix.

CHAPTER IV

BEYOND THE SOLAR SYSTEM

The stars, bright sentinels of the skies.

William Habington

IV. BEYOND THE SOLAR SYSTEM

WHEN THE NOVICE astronomer turns his attention to the stellar heavens, he is usually surprised to find that the stars are not all the same. Of course, all stars are luminous masses of radiant gas, but even a casual sweep of the heavens will reveal obvious differences in brightness and color among the stars. Spectral analysis reveals even more, the differing chemical compositions and temperatures of the stars.

Spectral Classification of the Stars

The stars are classified, in part, on the basis of their spectral analysis: what the spectroscope can tell about the star's temperature and chemical makeup. The principal research for these studies was carried out at Harvard College Observatory and this classification is, therefore, known as the Harvard System.

Briefly, there are eleven major categories in this system, denoted by the letters: W, O, B, A, F, G, K, M, R, N, and S. Stars are placed in one of these divisions on the basis of their spectra and the information revealed as to color, temperature, etc. The accompanying table indicates how the stars in each spectral class differ from each other.

The mnemonic device which astronomers use to memorize the order of the letters in the Harvard System reveals them to be very romantic people. The following phrases are used to fix the order of the Harvard System: "**W**ow! **O**h **B**oy! **A** **F**ine **G**irl. **K**iss **M**e **R**ight **N**ow, **S**weetie."

CLASSIFICATION OF STARS BY THE HARVARD SYSTEM *

SPECTRAL CLASS	STAR COLOR (VISUAL)	TEMPERATURE DEGREES F.	TYPICAL STARS
W	Greenish-White	62,000 °F.	Wolf-Rayet
O	Greenish-Blue	62,000 °F.	Gamma Velorum
B	Blue	44,000 °F.	Rigel
A	White	20,000 °F.	Sirius
F	Yellowish-White	12,000 °F.	Canopus
G	Yellow	10,000 °F.	The Sun
K	Orange	7,000 °F.	Antares
M	Red	4,900 °F.	Betelgeuse

* Types R,N, and S are not listed as they have spectra that are not readily interpreted. Stars in these classifications are relatively uncommon.

Magnitude

In addition to their spectral class, stars are classified according to their luminosity. This is expressed as the star's *magnitude.* Thus, the brighter stars are of the first magnitude, less bright stars are of the second magnitude, and so on. A star of the sixth magnitude is the faintest star that can be seen by the naked eye. A three-inch refractor will enable the observer to see stars of about the eleventh magnitude. The 200-inch reflector at Mount Palomar will pick up a star of the twentieth magnitude.

The given magnitude of a star usually implies its *apparent* magnitude: how bright it seems to an observer on Earth. Obviously, the apparent magnitude depends on two factors: the intrinsic brightness of the star and its distance from the observer.

To obtain a more accurate notion of the comparative brightness of stars, the idea of *absolute* magnitude comes into play. This value indicates the brightness that a star would have if *all* stars could be observed from the same distance.

In actual practice, it is the apparent magnitude of a star that is used as the descriptive value. Stars are measured to determine their magnitude by comparing them with stars of known magnitude. The table that follows lists several stars that are commonly used in comparison to determine magnitudes.

STARS OF KNOWN MAGNITUDE

STAR	CONSTELLATION	APPARENT MAGNITUDE
Arcturus	Boötes	0.2
Procyon	Canis Minor	0.5
Aldebaran	Taurus	1.1
Regulus	Leo	1.3
Bellatrix	Orion	1.7
Dubhe	Ursa Major	2.0
Alpheratz	Andromeda	2.2
Markab	Pegasus	2.6

Each division of magnitude represents a difference in brightness of 2½ times that of a neighboring division. If we assign a value of 100 to a 1st magnitude star, then a 2nd magnitude star will be 2½ times less bright and its value will be 40. A 3rd magnitude star will have a relative brightness of 40 divided by 2½ which is equal to 16. A star of the 6th magnitude, with a relative brightness of 1, is 100 times less bright than a 1st magnitude star.

All celestial objects, including the Sun, Moon, and the planets, are rated for brightness in terms of magnitude. Being closer to Earth, the solar system objects appear brighter to us than the stars and most are brighter than the first magnitude. This is indicated by a designation of *minus* magnitude. An object of magnitude — 1 is, therefore, 2½ times brighter than a zero magnitude object. On our relative brightness scale, it would have a value of

100 x 2½ x 2½ = 625.

The magnitudes of stars can be measured very exactly by modern astronomers. An instrument called a "photometer" is capable of measuring a star accurately to 1/100th of a magnitude or better. Many celestial almanacs will give the magnitude of stars precisely to the one-hundredth part of a magnitude. Thus, we might find an entry of: Spica — App. Mag. = 1.21. This indicates that the star, Spica, has an apparent magnitude which classifies it as somewhat fainter than a first magnitude star.

The table which follows indicates the magnitude and relative brightness of several familiar sky objects. In this table the scale of relative brightness is determined by assigning a value of 1.0 to a first magnitude star.

APPARENT BRIGHTNESS OF VARIOUS CELESTIAL OBJECTS *

Name of Object	Apparent Magnitude	Relative Brightness
Sun	−26.6	109,650,000,000
Moon (full)	−12.2	190,550
Venus	−4.28	129.4
Mars	−2.25	19.9
Sirius**	−1.58	10.7
Canopus	−0.86	5.55
Vega	0.14	2.21
Rigel	0.34	1.84
Betelgeuse	0.92	1.08
Antares	1.22	0.82
Polaris	2.12	0.36
Uranus	5.80	0.01

* Based on a value of brightness = 1.00 for a first magnitude star.
** The brightest visible star.

Main Sequence and "Abnormal" Stars

Most stars, on the basis of their luminosity (brightness) and temperature (spectral class), fit a standard pattern.

These stars are designated as main sequence stars and are considered normal. Certain stars do not fit this pattern and are considered to be "abnormal." The abnormals include such stars as the red giants, white dwarfs, Cepheids, RR Lyrae variables, long period variables, novae, and supernovae.

The red giants are enormous stars — hundreds of time larger than our Sun in some cases. They are low density stars, a factor responsible for their extremely large volume. The temperature of such stars is about 4,500° F. The star, Betelgeuse, is a red giant.

White dwarfs are relatively rare, but this may be due to their lack of brightness and the consequent difficulty of seeing them. In spite of their low luminosity, they have spectra that put them in the relatively "hot" group of white stars, Group A. The dwarfs are very small stars with high mass. A thimbleful of the matter of a white dwarf would weigh more than a ton. Sirius, which is a double star, has as its companion a white dwarf, Sirius B.

The variables and the Cepheids are stars whose brightness is not constant and changes from time to time. This variation in luminosity occurs periodically. The Cepheids were first discovered in the constellation for which they are named. However, these stars are found not only in Cepheus, but scattered throughout much of space. Variable stars of this nature are of importance to the astronomer as they are used in determining distances in deep space.

Another group of stars that differ from the main sequence stars are the novae and supernovae. A nova is a "new" star, but this does not mean that a star has been born — only that a star has suddenly increased tremendously in brightness. This sudden brightness is due to the actual explosion of the star, sending stellar dust and gas roaring out into the surrounding space.

Investigation indicates that apparently normal stars (main sequence) can, without warning, "blow their tops" in the awesome explosion that results in a nova. The question naturally arises as to the possibility of this occurring to our own Sun. G type stars such as ours do not, as a rule, become novae. Calculations suggest that the chances of this ever happening are only one in several billion.

Many novae have been discovered by amateur astronomers as they scan the sky for comets and meteor displays. A particularly rich field for the appearance of novae is the area of the Milky Way. Novae increase in light intensity so quickly that it is relatively easy for amateur astronomers to "discover" them. Novae, when they explode deep in space, often become brighter than any of the stars normally visible to the sky-watcher.

The supernova that exploded in 1054 was recorded by Chinese astronomers who observed that it was so brilliant that it could easily be seen in broad daylight. The wreckage of this blazing explosion still remains as a visible glowing gaseous cloud which we now call the Crab Nebula in the constellation Taurus.

The formation of a nova must be incredible — a stupendous stellar spectacle. Astronomers, however, recognize stellar explosions that are 10,000 times greater than an "ordinary" nova. These are known as supernovae. The true cause of these cosmic detonations is not fully known.

The Life And Death Of A Star

All of the star types discussed, the main sequence stars and the abnormals, represent different stages in the development of a star. Astronomers are able to construct a sequence of events which, they believe, traces the history of a star — from birth to death. The theoretical picture that they draw is constantly being revised, but somewhere in its shifting shape the story of the universe is to be found.

There must be a beginning — even in forming a star. And the beginning of a star originates in a mass of interstellar gas and dust — the basic stuff of which the universe is made. The birth process begins with local condensation of this interstellar matter into spheres of gas. These star nuclei build up their size by gravitational attraction of more gas and basic matter. The spheres, molded of cosmic gases, are the new stars.

They are cold stars; they do not yet glow. But as condensation increases and as gravitational forces bring about the contraction of matter, the temperature of the infant star starts to rise — the energy deriving from the forces of gravitation. It becomes a red giant with a surface temperature of 4,000° F. and a core of greater density and much higher temperature.

As the star ages, it finds a new source of energy — nuclear energy. A series of changes culminate in a thermonuclear reaction which changes hydrogen into helium. At this point the star has "grown up." It is a main sequence star.

In time the energy supply of the star is such that its brightness and temperature begin to increase. The hydrogen, at some time, will all be used up and nuclear energy will no longer be available to the star. Gravitational forces again must be the energy forces for the star as it starts to shrink and begins its decline. The star becomes dimmer and dimmer and contracts to a small dense mass of stellar material — a white dwarf.

As this highly compressed mass moves off into space, it cools off very quickly and soon darkens — a dead star — without light, without heat. Or, perhaps, another end may be in store for the dying star. Instead of fading into obscurity, some shrinking, cooling stars produce internal *vacuums*. Gases rush into the vacuum, producing intense temperatures and the star "blows up" ending its life cycle as a brilliant supernova!

Interstellar Distances

Many of the astronomer's theories about our universe are difficult to grasp. They stagger the mind. How can we conceive, in real terms, the incredible vastness of the universe the astronomer pictures? The answer, of course, is that we cannot, at least, not in terms which relate to our everyday experience.

To say that the Sun is 93,000,000 miles from Earth has, perhaps, some meaning for us in terms of distance. To say that Alpha Centauri, our nearest star, except for the Sun, is 25,000,000,000,000 miles away, is not really meaningful.

The mile as a unit of measure is inadequate to convey the idea of astronomical distances. Astronomers, therefore, use the idea of the "light year" to measure distance. This notion of using *time* to measure *distance* is not as curious as it sounds; we do it all the time. For instance, it is often said that New York is only five *hours* from Los Angeles by jet plane.

The same concept applies to the light year — the *distance* that light travels in the time of one year. A beam of light travels 186,000 miles in one *second*. A simple calculation shows the distance traveled in one year.

186,000 miles/second x 60 seconds/minute x 60 minutes/hour x 24 hours/day x 365¼ days/year = 1 light year = 5,880,000,000,000 miles

In terms of this measure of distance the Sun is the merest fraction of a light year away — 8 light *minutes*. Alpha Centauri, our nearest star, is 4½ light years away.

If we look up at the constellation of Andromeda, a faint, thin, cloudy patch of light can just barely be seen. This is the Andromeda Galaxy, an island universe, much like our own. The light that strikes our eye has been journeying across the deeps of space for many years, for the Andromeda Galaxy is about 1,500,000 light years away. It is a sobering thought to realize that the light we see emanating from this pinpoint in the sky left the galaxy a million and a half years ago — long before Man walked across the face of our planet.

The Galaxies

Although the stars seem to be randomly scattered in space, they actually exist in groups or communities of stars. Such a congregation of stars is called a galaxy. Our Sun and about 100 billion other stars form such a galaxy: the galaxy of the Milky Way.

The shape of this immense collection of stars is that of a lens with a spiral of arms circling outward from its rim, very much like a child's pinwheel. The Great Spiral Nebula in Ursa Major, shown in the photograph on page 101, affords a magnificent view of another galaxy which is similar to our own in general outline.

In the great galactic spiral of the Milky Way, measuring about 100,000 light years across, our Sun occupies a position about 30,000 light years from the center, near the equatorial plane of the galaxy. See Figure 37. Thus, when we look from the Earth along the equatorial plane of the galaxy, we see a hazy, luminous veil across the sky. We call it the Milky Way. This band with its nebulous glow is what we see as the result of the light of billions of stars in the center of the galaxy as we look from the Earth's position toward one edge.

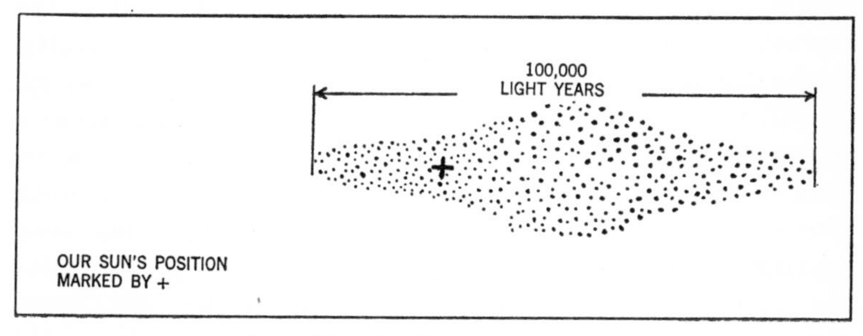

Figure 37. The Shape of our Galaxy

As astronomers probe into the depths of space with telescope and camera, they find more and more galaxies distributed in the "sea" of space like islands, each a universe within itself. These "island universes" are of different shapes and probably represent different stages in the life cycle of a galaxy. In Chapter VI, the relationship between the different kinds of nebulae and galactic evolution will be discussed.

How many galaxies are there in the universe? Calculations based on the relationship between space and mass suggest that the universe may have a diameter of 8,000,000,000 to 10,000,000,000 light years. In that space there are probably a billion galaxies! A billion star communities each with, perhaps, 300, to 500 billion stars! These are the concepts of the astronomers that jar the mind.

The Nature Of The Universe

What is the origin of the universe? What is its eventual destiny? These are the most intriguing questions that face the modern astronomer. Three theories have been advanced in an attempt to answer the unanswerable.

All theories of the nature of the universe are based on the seemingly indisputable fact that the galaxies, the island universes, are all moving away from each other into outer space. Furthermore, the galaxies farthest away are moving at greater speeds than those that are closer to us. How is this phenomenon explained?

The Belgian astronomer, Abbè Georges Lemaître suggested that the galaxies are all môving away from the site of a great cosmic explosion like the fragments of a bursting shell. The universe was created from a dense cloud of basic matter, reaching a temperature of, perhaps, a trillion degrees. Then, with a nuclear blast, the mass spread out from the center and as time went by began to condense into the separate clouds which made the stars and the galaxies.

Photograph from the Mount Wilson and Palomar Observatories.

Spiral nebula in Ursa Major — Messier 81. Photographed with the 200-inch Hale telescope.

The great British astronomer, Arthur Eddington once wrote, "The theory of the exploding universe is, in some respects, so preposterous that we naturally hesitate to commit ourselves to it. It contains elements so incredible that I feel almost an indignation that anyone should believe it — except myself."

A second theory, the theory of the pulsating universe, is really an extension of the first. It states that the outrushing galaxies will eventually reach a limit of expansion in space. They will slow down, stop, and begin a return to the center of the universe. There, crowding together, with temperatures rising, they will condense once more into a cloud of basic matter. The forces that brought on the original explosion will again propel the stuff of the universe outward into space and the process will be repeated.

The third theory is the most difficult to visualize and yet most modern opinion seems to favor it. It is the work, principally, of the British cosmologists: Fred Hoyle, Hermann Bondi, and Thomas Gold.

This theory, the continuous universe theory, suggests that the galaxies farthest out from the center of the universe are traveling at steadily accelerating speeds — at velocities approaching the speed of light. Einstein's theory holds that no body can *reach* the speed of light, as at that point the mass of the body becomes infinite. But, say these astro-physicists, the galaxies eventually *do* reach the speed of light and at that point they *disappear!* Wisely, perhaps, the theory does not explain where they disappear *to*.

The mass of the galaxies is not lost, however. The mass of the universe tends to remain constant. Thus, the mass of the disappearing galaxies reappears at the center of the universe where new galaxies are constantly being evolved from the new mass. These galaxies begin to rush outward into space and the whole process begins again: a universe that continually renews itself at the center with new energy derived from its oldest inhabitants.

There is nothing fixed or settled about the state of modern cosmology or astronomy. As new discoveries are made, our view of the kind of universe we inhabit is altered, modified or radically changed. The discovery of unusual space objects, such as the puzzling bodies called quasars, seems to raise new questions rather than resolve old ones.

Fred Hoyle, in the light of new discoveries revealed by the radio-telescope, has modified his continuous or steady-state theory of the universe. This great cosmologist now seems to lean towards a view based on the pulsating universe concept. It would seem that many exciting developments lie ahead for astronomers before they can create a valid picture of how our universe is really constructed.

CHAPTER V

CONSTELLATIONS: TRAIL MARKERS AMONG THE STARS

Many a night from yonder ivied casement,
ere I went to rest,
Did I look on great Orion sloping slowly
to the west.

Tennyson

V. CONSTELLATIONS: TRAIL MARKERS AMONG THE STARS

History Of The Constellations

THE STAR PATTERNS, by which we find our way around the sky, were very familiar to the ancient sky-watchers. The names they gave to the constellations lead us to expect to see, arching above us, a fantastic array of animal outlines. We should be able to find two bears, a swan, a whale, a dragon, a crane, a lion, a winged horse, a giraffe, and many others. Kings and queens, great heroes, and strange instruments are supposedly sketched in the heavens. Ancient folk myths tell wonderful stories of how the places in the sky came to be filled by this strange world of people and animals. Ptolemy listed forty-eight named constellations in his famous catalogue of the heavens.

Today, an observer would need to possess a magnificent imagination and a vast knowledge of folklore to perceive the mythical forms seen by the ancients. As a matter of fact, we now recognize a total of 88 constellations and it is fortunate, indeed, that we do not need to see them as the outlines of strange animals and people. Star charts and constellation maps show the stars of the constellations and delineate their boundaries, but no attempt is made to picture the outlines of a serpent or a scorpion.

How To Know And Find The Constellations

The serious student of astronomy must become acquainted with the constellations, particularly those that

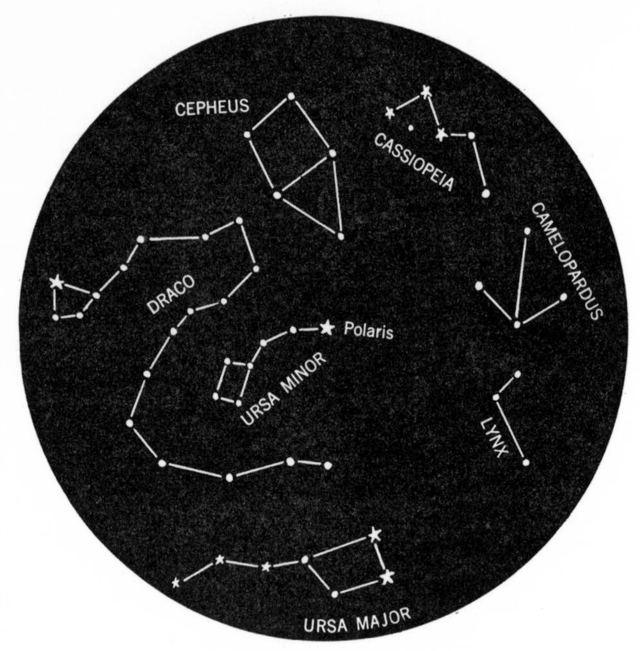

Figure 38. The Circumpolar Constellations

are visible from his point on the Earth's surface. This process can begin, simply enough, by learning to identify the circumpolar stars.

Some stars rise from below the horizon, move westward across the sky, and set. There are some stars, however, that move in their courses so close to the celestial pole that they never set. These are the circumpolar stars and can be seen every night of the year. Figure 38 shows the circumpolar stars visible to an observer in latitudes of 40° North.

The Big Dipper or Great Bear (Ursa Major) is the key constellation in this group. Nearly everyone knows the Big Dipper with its seven bright stars. Figure 39 shows the Dipper and the names of the stars of which it is composed. Note that Mizar has a smaller companion star, Alcor, close to it. These names are Arabic in origin, and

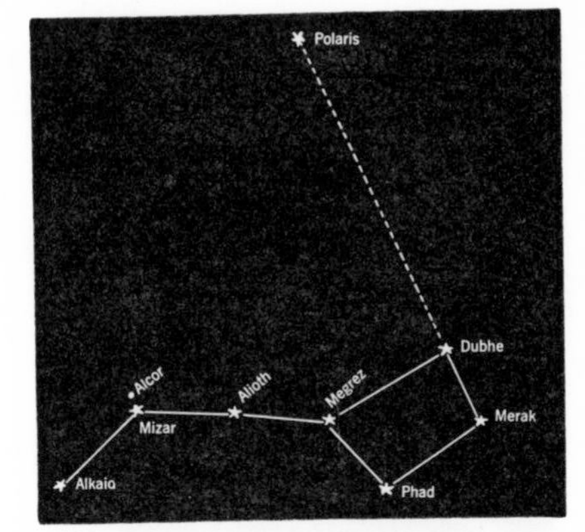

Figure 39.
The Stars of the
Big Dipper

Mizar means "the Horse" and Alcor, "the Rider."

The Big Dipper helps us find our way to Polaris, the star that lies almost directly at the North Celestial Pole. Dubhe and Merak are called the "Pointers", as a line running through them, and extending for about five times the distance between them, points to Polaris. The Pole Star is the first star in the handle of the Little Dipper. With these constellations identified, it is a simple matter to recognize the other circumpolar constellations. Draco, however, is composed of a trail of relatively faint stars and is somewhat difficult to trace. Fortunately, Draco is not one of the important constellations for the beginner to master.

In the winter sky, the Big Dipper must take second place to Orion which, unfortunately, is not circumpolar at 40° North. Orion is, undoubtedly, the finest constellation in the northern heavens. It contains some of the more interesting stars and within its boundaries are to be found some of the most fascinating celestial phenomena. In addition, Orion serves as the chief reference point in the winter sky. See Figure 40. Betelgeuse is a red giant star and is of the first magnitude. Rigel, diagonally opposite, is brighter than a first magnitude star. The three stars in a line form the famous Belt of Orion. Betelgeuse, from the Arabic, means "Armpit of the Giant."

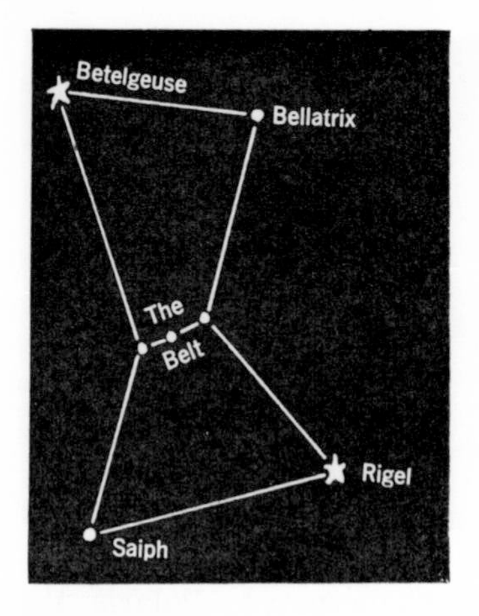

Figure 40.
The Constellation of Orion

Orion is a great trail marker in the northern sky. See Figure 41. The three stars in the Belt point south to Sirius, the Dog Star — the brightest star in the heavens. The stars of the Belt point north to Aldebaran in the constellation Taurus: a first magnitude star as red as Betelgeuse. The ancients depicted Aldebaran as the red eye of Taurus, the Bull. Then, from Aldebaran, it is but a step to the Seven Sisters, the Pleiades.

There are other ways to use Orion to spot the neighboring stars. Saiph and the first star in the Belt make a line that points north to Capella. A line between Betelgeuse and Bellatrix leads the eye to Procyon.

This, in brief, is the method by which the constellations serve as "road maps" of the heavens. The amateur who wishes to explore, with his telescope, the hundreds of intriguing celestial objects that lie within the scope of his lens, must know the constellations as he knows the streets and bypaths near his home. The star charts in this book will help the beginning sky-watcher to inaugurate his studies of the trail markers of the heavens.

In time, however, the serious student will require more detailed charts. One of the best is *Norton's Star Atlas*, which contains 18 star charts and lists 500 interesting

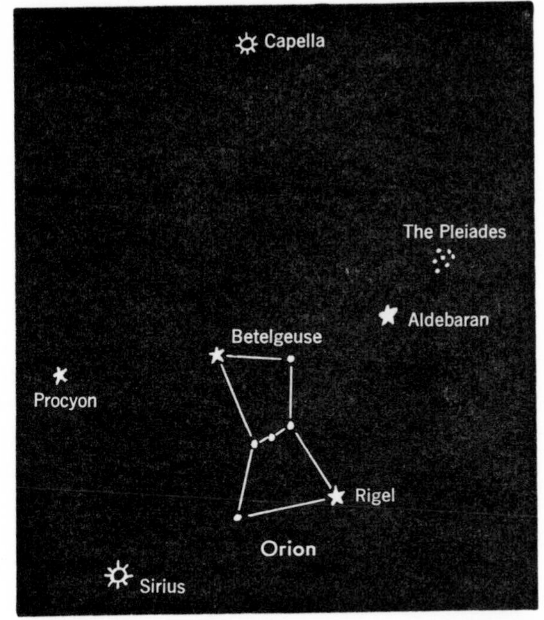

Figure 41.
Orion—
The Trail Marker

celestial objects. Perhaps, the finest of the star atlases is the beautifully color printed *Atlas Coeli* of Antonin Becvar. It lists 35,000 celestial objects and has a plastic overlay of the celestial grid coordinates. Every interested observer will want to refer to this magnificent atlas.

Using Constellations To Find Stars

Many of the stars have been given specific names, but these form only a small fraction of those that lie within reach of the sky-watcher's lens. It becomes necessary, therefore, to develop a system of identifying stars that can be applied to *all* of the important visible stars.

The method in use today is that proposed by Bayer, who compiled a famous star catalog in 1603. He assigned a Greek letter to each of the main stars of a constellation,

THE GREEK ALPHABET

α	Alpha	ι	Iota	ρ	Rho
β	Beta	κ	Kappa	σ	Sigma
γ	Gamma	λ	Lambda	τ	Tau
δ	Delta	μ	Mu	υ	Upsilon
ε	Epsilon	ν	Nu	φ	Phi
ζ	Zeta	ξ	Xi	χ	Chi
η	Eta	o	Omicron	ψ	Psi
θ	Theta	π	Pi	ω	Omega

using the first letter, Alpha, for the *brightest* star of the group and the last letter, Omega, for the *dimmest* star of the constellation. The Greek alphabet, and the corresponding English names are listed on this page.

Each star in a constellation has a two part name. A "first" name consisting of the Greek letter assigned because of its relative brightness, and a "last" name based on the constellation in which the star is found.

It is customary to use the genitive Latin name of the constellation in which the star is found in order to obtain the star's "last" name. For example, Regulus (Alpha Leonis) is immediately identified, by its name, as the brightest star in the constellation Leo; Mizar (Zeta Ursa Majoris) is the *sixth* brightest star in the Big Dipper.

Now, in addition to the Greek alphabet, the student astronomer must master the genitive Latin names of the constellations. There is more to astronomy, it seems, than meets the eye.

In the course of assigning letters under the Bayer system, certain errors have been made in the past so that sometimes the brightest star of a constellation has been given the name of the second letter (Beta) instead of the first. This has led to some confusion, but this traditional system is still universally employed. For instance, in the constellation Orion, the brightest star is Rigel (magnitude 0.34). Bayer, in error, named it Beta Orionis.

Betelgeuse, on the other hand, not as bright (magnitude 0.92), was designated as Alpha Orionis. Bayer's system has one further drawback in that only 24 stars can be named with the letters of the Greek alphabet. At times this is not sufficient to cover all the stars of a constellation.

An alternate system, proposed by Flamsteed, the first Astronomer Royal of England, assigns a number to each star in a constellation. The number "1" is assigned to the star in least right ascension and the system continues from there. This explains why some stars are designated by more than one name. Thus, Vega is also known as Alpha Lyrae (Bayer system) and as 3 Lyrae (Flamsteed's number).

A table of all the constellations, including the genitive names and other information is to be found in the Appendix.

CHAPTER VI

DOUBLE STARS, STAR CLUSTERS, NEBULAE, GALAXIES, AND VARIABLE STARS

The stars, stand as thick as dewdrops
on the fields of heaven.

P. J. Bailey

VI. DOUBLE STARS, STAR CLUSTERS, NEBULAE, GALAXIES, AND VARIABLE STARS

Multiple Stars

THE STAR, Mizar, at the bend in the handle of the Big Dipper, was sometimes called the "Proof" by the ancient Arabic astronomers. It was considered to be a test of good eyesight to be able to see its dimmer companion star, Alcor. Actually, it isn't much of a test, for anyone with reasonably good eyesight can see Alcor on a clear night. The curious thing, however, is that the telescope will show that Mizar is not a single star, but is in itself a "double."

Such multiple stars are quite common in the heavens and the telescope will reveal that many stars which appear, to the naked eye, to be single, can be resolved into two or more component stars. "Splitting doubles" with a telescope is an absorbing activity on the observation schedule of many star-gazers. Some of the color combinations to be seen in these multiple stars are quite beautiful.

There are, in general, two kinds of double stars. One type is called an optical double and is not a true double star. This phenomenon occurs when two stars lie in the same line of sight, but are actually separated by considerable distance in space. This may be illustrated by the following analogy:

While looking at the Moon, an observer sees a flashing light very close to the Moon's disc. He realizes, after a moment, that this is the light of an airplane that is following a course which lies across his line of sight to the

Moon. The airplane, of course, is a quarter of a million miles from the Moon, but its light, at that moment, seems but inches away from the Moon's edge. Stars which appear to be doubles, but which, in reality, merely lie along the same line of sight are known as *optical* doubles. They are relatively uncommon.

True doubles consist of a pair of stars revolving around a common center of gravity. True doubles are called *binary doubles* or binary stars. Binary, simply means having two parts or two components. There is often considerable contrast between the component stars with respect to brightness, size, and color which makes them particularly interesting as sky objects worthy of study.

An interesting example of such a binary is Antares (Alpha Scorpii), a red giant. A four-inch refractor will "split" Antares to reveal that it is a double. The companion is much smaller, with a greenish glow that contrasts beautifully with the brilliant red star.

Many observers consider the finest double star to be Albireo (Beta Cygni). A small telescope shows Albireo as a star of golden-yellow color with its companion star a strongly contrasting greenish-blue, an impressive double and a real showpiece in the heavens.

When one of the stars of a binary pair is noticeably of smaller magnitude than the other, the smaller is denoted as the *companion* star.

Some observers use double stars to test the quality of their telescopes, as has been previously mentioned in Chapter II. This is actually a test of the resolving power of the lens or mirror, which serves as the objective. Double stars are separated by a distance measured in an angle of arc. The Dawes Limit for a specific lens indicates the angular distance between objects that a lens should, theoretically, be able to distinguish. Thus, Rigel (Beta Orionis) should be split with a two-inch refractor and a three-inch lens of good quality should be able to resolve the double star, Polaris (Alpha Ursa Minoris). A

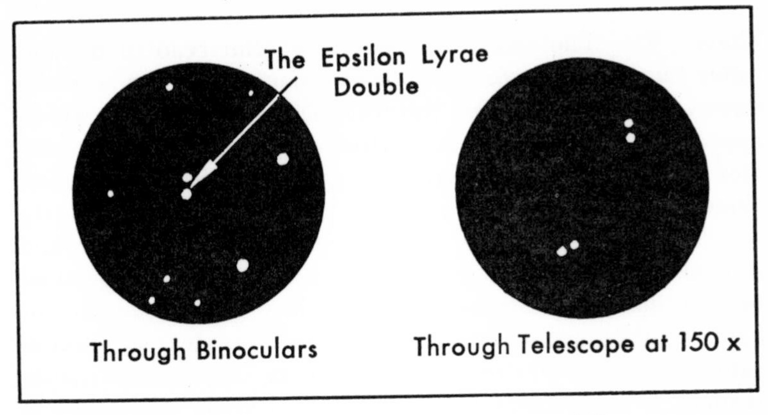

Figure 42. Epsilon Lyrae—The " Double-double "

list of test double stars has been included in Chapter II.

The star-gazer who is interested in double stars will want to split Epsilon Lyrae. This is not difficult as a pair of binoculars will do it easily. However, if Epsilon Lyrae is observed in the telescope at about 150 X, it will be seen that each of the "components" is also a double star Then the observer will be able to boast of splitting his first "double-double." See Figure 42. The famous Trapezium in Orion, Theta Orionis, is another quadruple star that is extremely popular as a telescope object among sky-watchers.

A table of interesting double stars and their locations is to be found in the Appendix. In addition, the notes that accompany the star charts indicate double stars along with other interesting celestial objects.

Star Clusters

There are few stellar telescope objects that can compete with a fine star cluster for sheer magnificence. Star clusters are, basically, groups of stars crowded, more or less, closely together. These clusters are of two types: open clusters and globular clusters.

An easily located open cluster is the Pleiades. See

Figure 41. The stars in this cluster can readily be seen with the naked eye and most people will be able to count six of the "Seven Sisters." This little family grows considerably larger when a pair of binoculars, or a telescope at low power, is trained upon it. Now dozens and dozens of stars leap into view, glittering sharply in the field of the telescope. This jewel-like open cluster is a fine telescope object that can be picked up easily, even by inexperienced observers.

Another good open cluster is the Hyades, a group of stars clustered around the red giant, Aldebaran (Alpha Tauri). This cluster is best observed with binoculars as even at low power it will not all be included in the field of the telescope. Hundreds of similar clusters are known and may be found by referring to the notes that accompany the star charts.

Much less common are the splendid globular clusters — glowing bursts of densely packed stars in incredible numbers. A large globular may contain as many as 100,000 stars, much concentrated in the center and thinning out rapidly at the edge of the cluster.

To the naked eye, or even with binoculars, a globular cluster appears as a tiny, filmy smudge — glowing dimly. Globular clusters are objects of deep space and all are very distant; none are closer than several thousand light years away. A telescope of moderate power transforms one of these misty patches into an unforgettably resplendent spectacle.

In the constellation Hercules can be found one of the best of the globulars — M 13. The photograph on page 121, taken with the 200-inch telescope at Mount Palomar, gives some idea of the fantastic concentration of stars that make up the "Great Cluster" of Hercules.

The notation, M 13, stands for — Messier 13. Charles Messier (1730-1817), a French astronomer, prepared a catalogue of certain celestial objects which he considered

Photograph from the Mount Wilson and Palomar Observatories.

The great globular star cluster in Hercules — Messier 13.

confusing or misleading. Messier was a tireless seeker after comets, periodic visitors from outer space that sometimes sweep through our solar system. Comets approaching from a great distance appear, at first, as hazy patches, much like globular clusters or nebulae.

Messier, often mistaking these nebulous blurs for comets, listed their positions and indicated that they were objects to be avoided when searching for comets. Messier's Catalogue of Nebulae and Clusters lists some of the finest nebular objects in the Northern Celestial Hemisphere. His catalogue is reproduced as a table in the Appendix.

Today, ironically enough, Messier is not remembered for the comets he discovered, but rather for his catalogue of 107 celestial objects "to be avoided while seeking comets."

Clusters and nebulae are also catalogued in a much more detailed publication. This most comprehensive listing was drawn up in 1888 by a Danish astronomer, J.E.L. Dryer. It is known as the *New General Catalogue*, and objects in this catalogue are assigned numbers preceeded by the letters "NGC." Thus, the "Great Cluster" in Hercules — Messier 13 — is also designated as NGC 6205.

Nebulae

Some of the dim, misty patches in the sky remain, in most telescopes, unresolved into clusters of stars. These were called nebulae, derived from the Latin word for "mist" or "cloud". The true nature of these nebulae was not discovered until the great modern telescopes began to extend their explorations into the depths of space.

The telescope, the astro-camera, and the spectroscope made the unexpected discovery that there are more than stars in deep space. Within our universe, there are great, hazy masses of dust and gas — the misty matter of the great nebulae. These masses of dispersed stellar material are called *diffuse nebulae*. The diffuse nebulae are

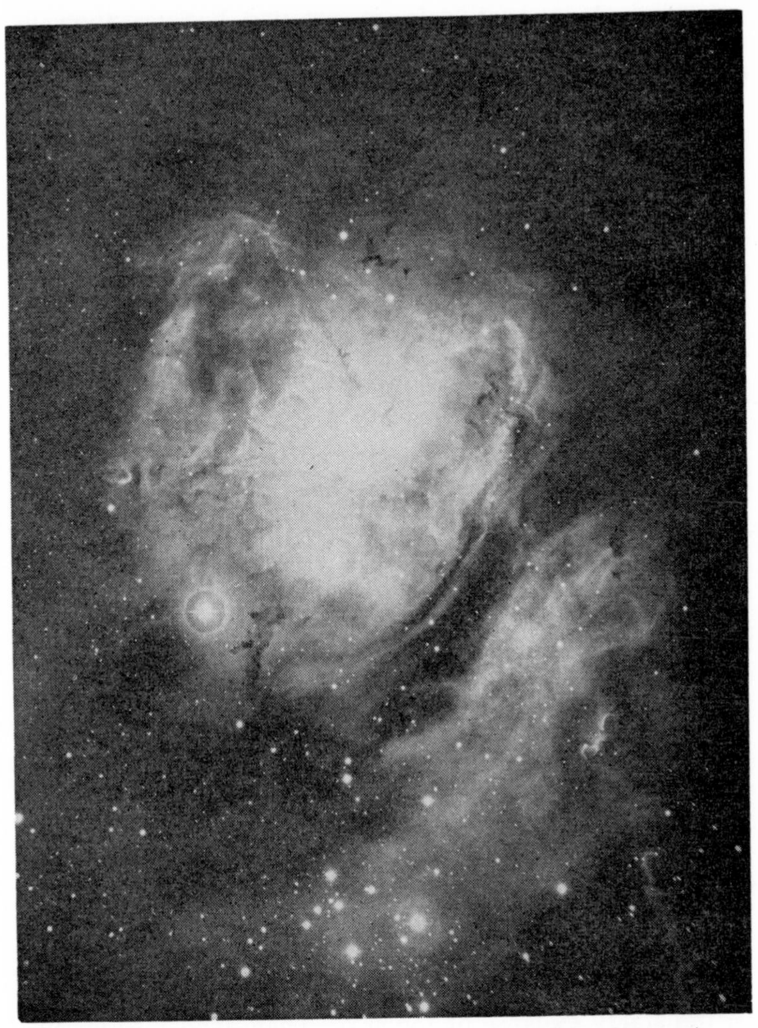

Photograph from the Mount Wilson and Palomar Observatories.

The diffuse nebula in Sagittarius, known as the "Lagoon" nebula or Messier 8.

sometimes known as *galactic* nebulae because they lie within the boundaries of our own island universe — the Galaxy of the Milky Way.

Diffuse nebulae may be bright or dark. Bright, because the luminous clouds of gas glow with the reflected light of the stars in their interior; dark, because the masses of dust and gas are not illuminated by any stars in their central core.

A beautiful example of a bright diffuse nebula is the so called "Lagoon Nebula" (Messier 8), in the constellation Sagittarius. The photograph on page 123 clearly reveals the shimmering, luminous gas cloud — glowing with the light of the stars in its heart.

Modern theory suggests that these nebulae are related to the process of star formation. The spectroscope indicates that the nebulae are composed largely of hydrogen, helium, and ionized oxygen. This is the basic stuff of which the stars are made. It is not too unlikely to assume that the stars glowing within these nebulous masses have been born as condensations of the stellar dust and gas of the cloud that surrounds them.

The "Lagoon Nebula" may be readily seen in the constellation of Sagittarius. Norton's Star Atlas notes, "— visible to the naked eye. An ill-defined nebulosity with dark patches and stars, followed by an irregular open cluster." This nebula is not too difficult to locate with the help of star charts. But do not expect it to look like the photograph unless you are using a 200-inch telescope.

The dark nebulae give the appearance of black holes in the starry expanse of the sky. They appear so because their opaqueness blocks off and interferes with the light of the stars that are shining behind them. A particularly fine example of a dark nebula is the "Horsehead Nebula" in Orion. This murky, unilluminated cloud, reminiscent of a horse's head or a chess knight, may be seen in the

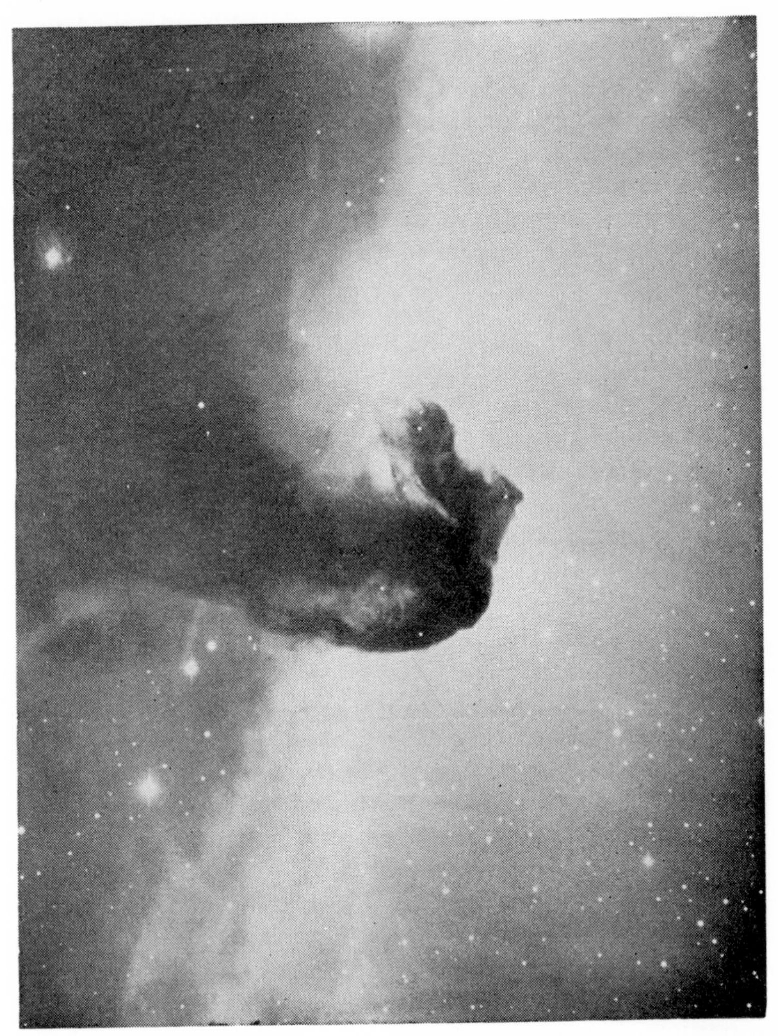

Photograph from the Mount Wilson and Palomar Observatories.

The "Horsehead" nebula in Orion. Photographed in red light by the 200-inch Hale telescope.

photograph on page 125. It can be readily observed that the dark bulk of the nebula is preventing the light of the stars behind it from reaching the observer. Many such dark patches exist in the sky and it was not until quite recently that astronomers had any real notion of what they might be. In the Southern Celestial Hemisphere, an even more spectacular dark nebula — the Coal Sack — may be seen by observers in those latitudes.

Galaxies

The great telescopes of the modern era were responsible for some observations about our universe that have staggered the minds of men. They found, for instance, that some of the cloudy, nebulous patches do not lie within our own galactic universe at all! Instead of being filmy clouds of gas, these nebulae were shown to be immense concentrations of stars, star kingdoms that are separate universes — actual galaxies much like our own.

The "extra-galactic" nebulae" — so called because they lie outside the boundaries of our galaxy — these "nebulae" are not nebulae at all, but island universes of billions of stars, each an entity in itself.

Many galaxies (nebulae) can be observed with telescopes of small or moderate power. However, only very large telescopes and photographic techniques will resolve these immense clouds into the actual stars of which they are composed.

Galactic nebulae are best observed on dark, moonless nights. The telescope must be set up in an area where there is no interference from city lights. The great nebulae in Andromeda and Orion can be seen under almost any conditions but total darkness will improve the likelihood of spotting some of the lesser known galactic clouds. The area of the sky north of Spica in the constellation Virgo is a rich field for the observation of nebulae.

Many of these nebulosities have been revealed by the astro-camera to possess the same shape as our own —

Photograph from the Mount Wilson and Palomar Observatories.

Spiral nebula — NGC 2403. An extra-galactic "nebula" in the Constellation of Camelopardus.

great, spinning, multi-armed spirals of billions of stars. Such a spiral galaxy is the spiral "nebula" in the constellation Camelopardus — NGC 2403. It may be seen in the photograph on page 127. Another fine spiral is the one in Ursa Major — Messier 81. Its photograph appears on page 101.

Not all galaxies are spiral shaped. Some are shaped like spindles, some are ellipses, others are irregular in shape, but each one is speeding outward into deep space, each one an entire universe, each one the cradle of a thousand million suns.

Variable Stars

One area where the dedicated amateur can make valuable contributions to astronomical research is in the observation of variable stars. A variable star is one whose brightness or magnitude changes in the course of a period of time.

Some stars vary in brightness because they are really doubles. The variation in light output occurs as one member of the pair passes in front of the other, eclipsing it, and reducing the amount of light reaching the observer.

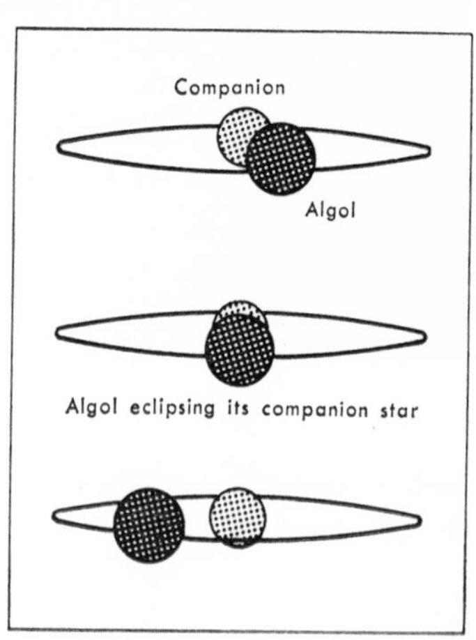

Figure 43.

Algol—An eclipsing binary star

As they revolve around a common center, the eclipsed component passes from behind its companion and the light again increases. Such a star system is known as an *eclipsing variable binary* and the period of variation depends on the rate at which the two stars revolve around their common center.

The best example of such an eclipsing variable binary is Algol (Beta Persei). The period of variation of Algol is 2.75 days and the light is dimmed for about four hours, which is the length of time it takes for one component to eclipse the other. See Figure 43. The name, Algol, means "demon" in Arabic. The ancient astronomers must have been puzzled and awed by the strange behavior of this star that "winked" at them from the sky.

Pulsating variables are less easily explained. These stars gradually increase in brightness, reach a peak, and then pale to their minimum magnitude. The star Mira (Omicron Ceti) has a minimum brightness of the 10th magnitude. Over a period of 150 days it reaches the brilliance of a 3rd magnitude star before fading to its minimum value again. Incidentally, Mira is another Arabic name, meaning "miracle star."

Much can be determined of stellar structure and evolution by studying variable stars. The interested amateur should write to the American Association of Variable Star Observers, 4 Brattle Street, Cambridge, Massachusetts. This dedicated group of amateurs, who sponsor other observation programs as well, are recognized as having made distinct contributions to current astronomical theory.

CHAPTER VII

VISITORS TO OUR SKIES

Old men and comets have been reverenced for the same reason: their long beards, and pretences to foretell events.

Jonathan Swift

VII. VISITORS TO OUR SKIES

Comets

ONE of the surest paths to astronomical "fame" is to discover a comet. For, by custom, any new comet is named after the first person to record its appearance. Perhaps this is why the indefatigable Messier spent much of his life seeking these elusive visitors to our skies.

A big comet, sweeping close to the Earth, puts on an impressive display. The head of the comet glows brilliantly and a filmy tail sometimes streams out behind it. The comet, a huge concentration of tiny particles of dust and glowing gas, approaches the Sun on a long, looping orbit. As it nears the Sun, its brilliance increases for the comet glows only as a result of the reflected light of the Sun.

The comet's tail lengthens more and more as its orbit brings it closer and closer to the Sun. The tail of the comet always points away from the Sun, a phenomenon which is probably due to the pressure of solar radiation. See Figure 44.

The head of a comet is known as a *coma* and it may contain a bright, flaring nucleus of condensed material. Some comets are truly enormous with comas almost a million miles in diameter.

The tail, and it should be noted that some comets never develop tails, is a very thin drift of gaseous material trailing after the comet's head. So thin is a comet's tail that it is possible to see the background stars

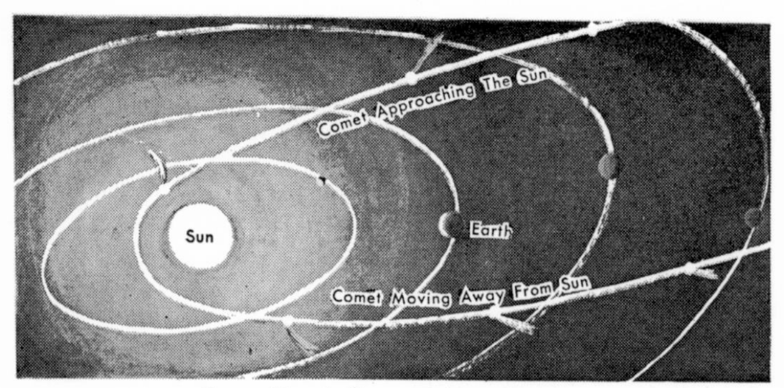

Figure 44. A Comet Orbiting The Sun

shining through it. In the past when comets of considerable size have passed close to the Earth, some people have been fearful of the possibility of "collision" between the Earth and the fiery comet. It is amusing to note that the Earth has passed several times through the tails of comets without anyone but astronomers being aware of it, so thin is the nebulous material of a comet's tail.

The tails of some comets are truly spectacular, stretching out for, perhaps, 50 to 100 million miles across the sky. The photograph on page 135 is of Cunningham's Comet. Note the star trails.

The comets which pay regular visits to our solar system are known as periodic comets. The most famous, of course, is Halley's Comet, which makes its journey around the Sun once every 76 years. It was last seen in 1910 and should appear once more in our skies in 1986.

Evidence seems to indicate that comets are, in some way, associated with showers of meteors. The famous case of Biela's Comet emphasizes the link between meteors and comets. Biela discovered the comet in 1826 and plotted its period of return as 6¾ years. It was observed for several returns and then, astonishingly, it separated into a pair of comets. In 1866 Biela I and Biela II did not return. Instead a brilliant shower of meteors appeared in the sky in the exact place where the comet had been

Photograph from the Mount Wilson and Palomar Observatories.

Comet Cunningham, December 21, 1940.

expected. This kind of meteor display seems to be associated with several of the periodic comets.

Comet-seeking is an interesting pastime that the amateur sky-watcher can engage in profitably. Of course, he may spend a lifetime without finding a new comet, but the chance of discovery is always there. In any case, he will learn a good deal about the sky in the process of scanning for comets.

A wide field and low magnification is the most effective combination when looking for comets. The sky-watcher should select a specific region in the sky and make slow, overlapping horizontal sweeps with the telescope, examining carefully the celestial objects that slowly drift across the field of his instrument.

Comets will appear as faint misty patches in the dark field of the sky. Unfortunately, however, so do star clusters and nebulae. Therefore, each time such a nebulosity is sighted, the comet seeker must check his star catalogues to see if the object has been previously located and identified.

If it *is* a new object, a precise picture of its position, with relation to the surrounding stars, must be drawn. Comparison observations are then made over a period of time and if motion is detected, the object is likely to be a comet. If no record of a comet in that location exists, then a new discovery has been made. The observer should report this, by telegram, to the nearest observatory for verification. And so, fame, of a sort, may be achieved.

Meteors

The thin, fiery streak of a "shooting star" is a familiar sight in the heavens. The streaks are the trails of stony or metallic particles that speed through the Earth's atmosphere at velocities of 40 miles per second. Air friction at this speed heats the particle to glowing incandescence anl its trail is marked by a brief, arcing flash of light. This, of course, is not a shooting star, but a meteor.

These bits of debris from outer space are not large. A particle the size of a pea will produce a very respectable fire trail.

Most meteors are vaporized by heat long before they reach the surface of the Earth. Some meteors, however, survive this ordeal by fire and fall upon the Earth without being entirely consumed. Those that reach the Earth are called, *meteorites or aerolites.*

Meteorites have a smooth, molten look on the outside and are usually made up of stone, iron, nickel, cobalt or a combination of these substances. It is estimated that about a ton of meteorites fall upon the Earth each day, ranging in size from that of a grain of dust to that of a baseball.

Occasionally a very large meteor strikes the Earth and the results can be devastating. In Siberia, an entire forest was flattened as a result of a meteor strike, while in Arizona one can see Meteor Crater — an awesome hole that has been blasted out of the earth.

Large particles which move at relatively slow speeds through the atmosphere make a billiant display. They are known as "fireballs" and their trails may last for several seconds. Sometimes a fireball disintegrates in a series of sharp explosions as it approaches the Earth. Exploding fireballs are known as *bolides* and their celestial bombardment is a truly startling occurrence.

Although meteors can be seen at any time, they are most frequent at certain times of the year and in certain parts of the sky. These periodic, intense meteoric displays are called *meteor showers.* During the height of one of these showers, more than 100 meteors may be observed in the space of an hour.

The showers are named for the constellations in which they seem to originate. The meteors seem to radiate in all directions from one point in the constellation. This point is called the *Radiant* or Radiant point.

One of the most familiar showers is the shower of the Perseids, radiating from the constellation of Perseus in the early part of August. It is well worth making a special effort to see this fine display.

A table of important meteor showers, including dates and Radiant points, has been included in the Appendix.

Auroras

One of the phenomena of the night sky that can be enjoyed by any observer is the *aurora borealis* — the Northern Lights. A similar phenomenon, the *aurora australis*, is sometimes seen in southern skies.

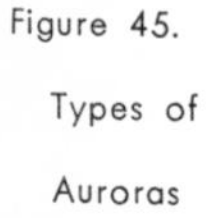
Figure 45. Types of Auroras

Auroras are probably the result of sunspot activity and the emission of charged particles from the Sun. The atmosphere glows, as its gases are ionized by cosmic radiation, much like a neon sign. The appearance of auroras usually coincides with the frequency and intensity of sunspot activity.

Auroras of many different types are known, and all are beautiful. Filmy, shifting masses of color may arc in broad bands across the sky. Milky greens, pinks, and reds waver in ribbon-like trails above the horizon. Colored rays of light pulse and flash like flames.

When recording auroras, the observer should note the type (See Figure 45), color, atmospheric conditions, size of the aurora, height above the horizon, and the time of the duration of each phase.

Zodiacal Light and Gegenschein

Similar to auroras are the aerial glows known as the Zodiacal Light and the Gegenschein. Sometimes, after dusk or before dawn, a faint, conical ribbon of light can be seen radiating upwards from the unseen Sun, the point of the cone tapering towards the zenith. As this glow extends along the band of the Zodiac, it is known as the Zodiacal light.

The Zodiacal Light does not seem to be an atmospheric phenomenon as is an aurora. It may be due to electrical disturbances or light reflected from a belt of tiny particles extending outward from the Sun and crossing the orbit of our own planet. The light usually appears white although some observers have reported a faint pinkish glow.

Rarely seen is the phenomenon known as the Gegenschein, sometimes called the Counterglow. It is always seen opposite the Sun in the sky and appears as a round luminous haze very much larger than the Moon. September is the best month for observation of the Gegenschein. Conditions of total darkness must prevail if the observer is to catch a glimpse of the elusive aerial glow of the Gegenschein.

CHAPTER VIII

PHOTOGRAPHING THE HEAVENS

No sight that the human eyes can look upon is more provocative of awe than is the night sky scattered thick with stars.

Llewelyn Powys

VIII. PHOTOGRAPHING THE HEAVENS

Methods and Equipment

AT the eyepiece of a great modern telescope, we are more likely to find a piece of photographic film than the eye of the astronomer. The reason is quite simple. The human eye records light instantaneously; it cannot accumulate it. A piece of light-sensitive film, on the other hand, will continue to react to light as long as it is exposed to it. During long time exposures, therefore, objects which are too faint to be visible to the naked eye have sufficient time to build up an image on the photographic plate. The astronomer can, with the aid of the astro-camera, reach farther into space than he can with the telescope alone.

The amateur will probably decide, eventually, to try his hand at photographing some of the objects in the sky. Successful astronomical photography is not easy to achieve, involving, as it does, considerable trial and error work until a satisfactory technique is evolved.

Simple astrophotography requires nothing more than a camera and a supporting tripod. If the camera is focused at infinity and pointed toward the North Star (Polaris) an interesting pattern of stars will appear as streaks on the film. These streaks are the paths of the stars and are called "star trails." As Polaris is the center of the celestial sphere, these star trails will appear to have a circular path.

To record star trails, point the camera on a tripod

at the North Star or at a familiar constellation such as Ursa Major or Orion and open the shutter for an exposure of ten minutes or longer. The length of the exposure is determined, to some extent, by the presence or absence of nearby city lights. Longer exposures may result in too much blackening of the film if city lights exert an interfering influence.

Meteors or "shooting stars" can be recorded if the photographer is patient. The secret is in knowing where to point the camera. As many meteor showers are recurrent at specific periods of the year, the knowledgeable photographer can prepare in advance to record these blazing visitors to our skies. The table of meteor showers included in the appendix gives the dates and the point in the sky from which we may expect displays of meteors.

Brilliant color photographs have been made of the strange auroras which show great variation of shape and color. Exposure with color film will vary depending on the brightness of the aurora and the atmospheric conditions. Exposures may be as short as 1/25th of a second but most photographs of auroras require longer exposures, ranging from 1 second to 5 minutes.

No hard and fast rules can be set down with the hope that they will apply under all circumstances. Much depends on the equipment available and on the abilities of the photographer. Some general techniques will be suggested here, with the purpose of letting the individual adapt them to his particular situation. Careful and persistent effort will be rewarded with photographs that can compete with those of the professional.

Three general methods are in use to couple cameras to telescopes for astrophotography. These methods are: prime focus, eyepiece projection, and eyepiece-camera.

The first two methods, prime focus and eyepiece

projection require a special astrocamera or a camera modified so that its lens can be removed and leave its shutter operable. Thus for the amateur astrophotographer the eyepiece-camera method is most strongly suggested. The camera must be attached to the telescope eyepiece by some kind of mounting bracket as indicated in Figure 46.

The method which lends itself most easily to the average situation is simply to take a picture of the image that the telescope eyepiece magnifies. Except for a device to hold the camera in position, this technique requires no modifications of existing equipment.

The first step is to focus the telescope on the object to be photographed. (Many amateurs find the Moon to be an excellent subject for their first attempts at astrophotography.) After the telescope is sharply focused, the camera lens is brought to the telescope eyepiece, focused on the image, and an exposure is made. This technique is illustrated in Figure 46.

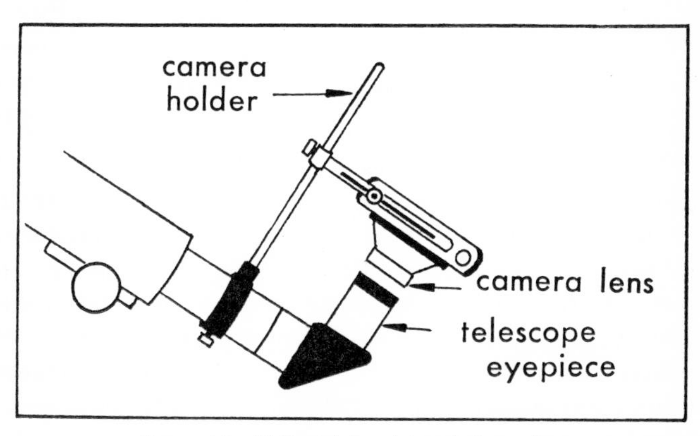

Figuse 46. Method I For Astro-photography

The slight gap between the telescope eyepiece and the lens of the camera may be a source of some difficulty, as extraneous light can enter the system at this point. The resulting flares, ghost images, and reflections can

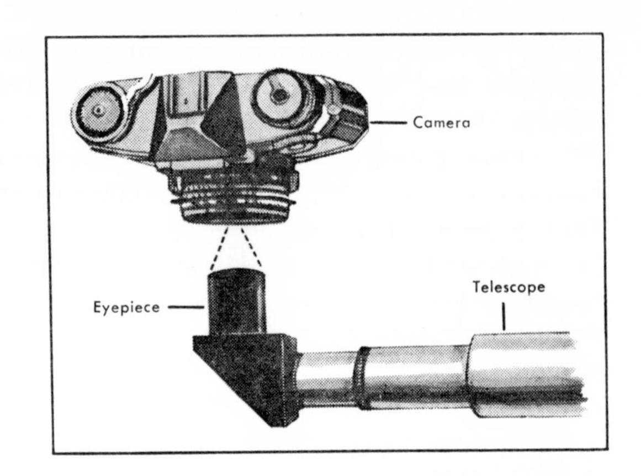

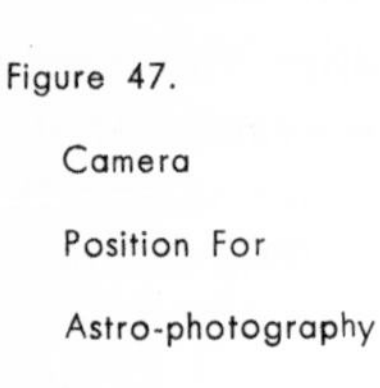
Figure 47. Camera Position For Astro-photography

spoil an otherwise successful photograph. This can easily be avoided by making a simple tube of black paper to fit loosely over the eyepiece of the telescope and the barrel of the camera lens.

In using this arrangement, the camera should be mounted on the tube of the telescope by means of a strut or bracket. Such a holder can be purchased as a separate telescope accessory.

It is essential that the camera be positioned above the telescope eyepiece at the point where the eyepiece focuses the image. The point where the eyepiece focuses the image is known as the *exit pupil* and may be seen in Figure 47 as the point where the beams of light (represented by dotted lines) meet and cross. The exit pupil for any eyepiece may be found by focusing the telescope on any object and holding a piece of tracing paper or wax paper behind the telescope eyepiece. By moving the paper back and forth slightly, a sharp picture, in miniature, will be cast by the eyepiece on to the paper. The point, where the tiny image is sharpest, is the exit pupil. The distance between the eyepiece and the exit pupil is known as the *eye relief.*

After having determined the location of the exit pupil, the camera is placed so that the exit pupil (of the eyepiece) falls at the diaphragm opening of the camera. The camera may then be carefully focused and the exposure made.

One factor that is vital in determining the proper exposure is to know the "f/" value of the system that is being used. The following calculation will determine this f/ number for any telescope-camera system. The following relationship holds true:

$$\text{f/ number} = \frac{\text{magnifying power of telescope}}{\text{objective size in inches}} \times \begin{matrix}\text{camera} \\ \text{focal length}\end{matrix}$$

For example, the f/ value, for a 2.5 inch refractor with a 45X eyepiece in combination with a two-inch focal length lens on a camera, is computed below.

$$\text{f/ number} = \frac{45}{2.5} \times 2.0 \text{ inches} = 18 \times 2 = 36$$

Therefore, in all calculations to determine exposure, the f/ value for this particular system will be f/ 36.

Focusing will depend on the type of camera used. A simple range set camera or range finder camera can be set at infinity and a test exposure made. With a reflex camera, the image is focused on the ground glass for maximum sharpness. If the camera has a removable film holder, a ground glass may be inserted in the plane of the film while the image is focused. Then, the ground glass is removed and the film holder is replaced for the exposure.

A second system for astro-photography dispenses with both the telescope eyepiece lens and the camera lens. The image of the telescope's objective lens is thrown directly on the film which must be located at the focal point of the telescope. This arrangement will provide for the greatest amount of light and the sharpest images.

However, it is necessary to provide an adapter which will couple the camera body to the eyepiece tube of the telescope. One end of the adapter should be threaded to

GENERAL EXPOSURE RECOMMENDATIONS FOR AMATEUR ASTROPHOTOGRAPHY

SUBJECT	INSTRUMENT	MOUNT	OBJECTIVE	f NUMBER	FILMS and PLATES	EXPOSURE (depending on conditions and brilliance)
Star Trails	Any camera	Rigid support	Any lens	Wide open	Fast, B&W and color	Up to 30 min or more
Meteors	Any good camera	Rigid support	Good lens	f6.3 or better	Fast and panchromatic	10-30 min
Aurorae	Camera with fast lens	Rigid support	Fast lens	f4 5 or better	Fast, B&W and color	1 sec to 5 min
Moon	Camera, or camera with telescope	Fixed or equatorial with or without drive	1" diameter or larger	About f12	Slow and panchromatic	1/100 sec to 10 sec
Stars and Comets	Camera, or camera with telescope	Equatorial with guiding sights	1" diameter or larger	f6.3 or better	Fast, B&W and color	10 min to 1 hr
Clusters and Nebulae Constellations	Camera, or camera with telescope	Equatorial with sights and drive	1" diameter or larger	About f6.3	Fast, B&W and color	10 min to 1 hr
Planets	Camera with telescope	Equatorial preferably with drive	1" diameter or larger for detail 6" and up	Use what you have	Fast, B&W and color	1/2 to 15 sec
Sun* (Never look at the sun with any optical device!)	Camera with telescope	Rigid or equatorial with or without drive	Neutral Density Filters 4.00-6.00 over 1" or larger main objective	f32-f64	Slow and panchromatic	1/1000-1/25 sec with Neutral Density Filters 4.00-6.00 over main optical objective (not the eyepiece!)
Man-Made Satellites	Any good camera	Rigid	Good lens	f4.5	Fast	Hold shutter open for duration of pass

COURTESY EASTMAN KODAK COMPANY

fit the lens mounting in the camera lens barrel, and the other end should have the same diameter as a telescope eyepiece, in order to fit into the eyepiece holder of the telescope. Figure 48 illustrates such an adapter.

With this system, the f/ value is the f/ value of the telescope alone and no special calculations are required. See chapter II for the method used to determine the f/ number for a telescope.

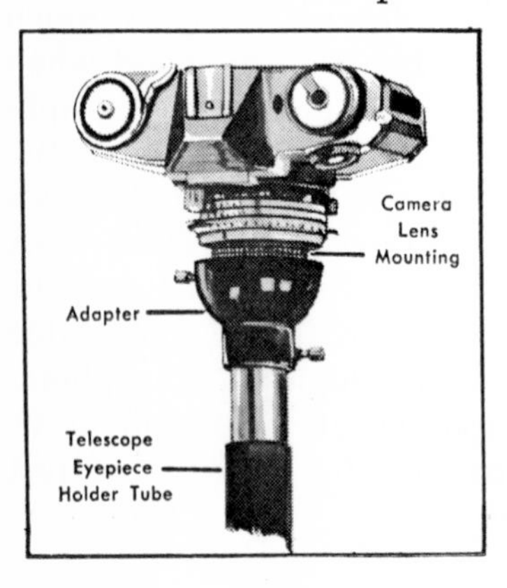

Figure 48.

Adapter For

Astro-photography,

Method II

The best type of camera for telescope photography is the 35 mm. single lens reflex camera. This film size is near the maximum that can be illuminated when using Method II for astro-photography. In addition, the ground glass focusing is a tremendous convenience in the first method discussed; in the second method, it is a necessity.

The one drawback in the use of 35 mm. single lens reflex cameras is that they tend to have a relatively violent shutter action, since many employ a focal plane shutter. As the shutter snaps across at the moment of exposure, the camera may be jarred or shaken with a consequent reduction of image sharpness. Some workers have found that better results are obtained if the shutter is held open at "time", and the exposure is made by waving a piece of cardboard in front of the telescope's objective to control the entrance of light.

Films and Exposure

Exposure is something that must be determined empirically for each tele-camera unit. Only by a careful series of test exposures will the astro-photographer arrive at a working technique that is right for him.

Films can be generally classified as "fast" films or "slow" films. The resolution of the fast films is relatively poor, whereas, the slow films are characterized by much higher resolving power. Slower films are employed when considerable light is available; for example, in photographing terrestrial objects, sunspots, or the surface of the Moon. Examples of such films are Eastman Kodak's Panatomic-X and High Contrast Copy Film. Their ASA ratings are 25 and 20, respectively. Such films may be exposed at twice their ASA value without appreciable deterioration of resolution or grain quality. For photographs of the Moon, a test exposure of ½ second at f/22 is, at least, a point of departure for a series of test pictures of the Moon's surface.

KODAK FILMS – ROLL AND SHEET*

	ROLL FILMS	ASA SPEED	35mm FILMS	ASA SPEED	SHEET FILMS	ASA SPEED
B&W	PANATOMIC-X (120 only)	40	PANATOMIC-X	32	PANATOMIC-X	64
	VERICHROME Pan	125	PLUS-X Pan	125	PLUS-X Pan (ESTAR Thick Base)	125
	TRI-X Pan	400	TRI-X Pan	400	SUPER-XX Pan	200
	ROYAL-X Pan (120 only)	1250	High Contrast Copy	—	Super Panchro-Press, Type B	250
			Infrared	—	TRI-X Pan (ESTAR Thick Base)	320
					ROYAL Pan	400
					RS Pan	650
					ROYAL-X Pan	1250
COLOR	KODACOLOR-X	64	KODACHROME II	25	EKTACHROME, Daylight	50
	EKTACHROME-X	64	KODACHROME-X	64	EKTACOLOR Professional, Type L	50
	EKTACHROME Professional (120 and 620 only)	50	KODACOLOR-X	64		
	High Speed EKTACHROME, Daylight (120 only)	160	EKTACHROME-X	64		
			High Speed EKTACHROME, Daylight	160		

COURTESY EASTMAN KODAK COMPANY

Faster films, such as Kodak's Tri-X, which is rated at ASA 200, but may be exposed at ASA 800 with good results, will permit shorter exposures. This is important, because in stellar photography moving objects are being photographed — the stars. At least, they appear to move as the Earth rotates under the celestial sphere.

The Earth's motion will be apparent in tele-camera exposures that are longer than ½ second. To photograph the stars, which are relatively dim, long exposures are necessary. The result is blurred images or star trails, such as have been mentioned previously.

The way to avoid this is to use an equatorial mounting, which permits the observer to follow the star by rotating the tele-camera on the polar axis of the mount. Clock drives can propel the tele-camera at the same rate as the Earth moves and the star is always kept in the center of the field.

The owner of a camera-telescope system which is mounted on an altazimuth base should attempt some stellar photography. If care is exercised, a "guide" star can be centered in the cross-hairs of the finder telescope and kept there by small adjustments, at suitable intervals, while the exposure is being made. At long exposures, minor movements, if smoothly done, will not affect the final photograph appreciably.

In the end, however, it is the ingenuity and persistence of the individual observer that will determine the quality of the work produced.

CHAPTER IX

TRACKING MAN-MADE SATELLITES

Equipped with his five senses, man explores the universe around him and calls the adventure Science.

Edwin P. Hubble

Courtesy National Aeronautics and Space Administration

Space Probe Satellite

IX. TRACKING MAN-MADE SATELLITES

MAN is beginning to populate the heavens with a variety of artificial satellites that open up new fields of observation for the amateur astronomer. More and more of these pioneering thrusts into space are achieving success, and soon the sky-watcher may be hard put to distinguish between the natural and the man-made.

Satellite Launching

The forces that sustain the flight of a satellite in space are, of course, the same forces that keep our Moon in orbit: the combination of the velocity of the Moon and the gravitational pull of the Earth.

The satellite is thrust upward from the Earth by the power of its rockets. If it were not for the Earth, its natural tendency would be to continue onward into space. This is Newton's First Law of Motion: a body remains in a state of uniform motion unless acted upon by an external force. But an external force, the gravitational pull of the Earth, tends to counteract the rocket's motion into space and tries to draw it back to the Earth from which it sprang. In the light of our everday experience, this is exactly what happens when we heave a stone into the air.

When a delicate balance between the speed of the satellite and the Earth's gravitational pull is achieved, the satellite will have too much speed to fall back to Earth, and not enough speed to throw off the effects of gravity and move off into outer space. The satellite, at that point, will be in "orbit."

The speed necessary to overcome completely the force of the Earth's gravity is known as the "escape velocity." This is about 7 miles per second or 25,000 miles per hour. To achieve "orbit velocity", that is, not enough speed to break away completely, the velocity of the satellite should be on the order of about 18,000 miles per hour.

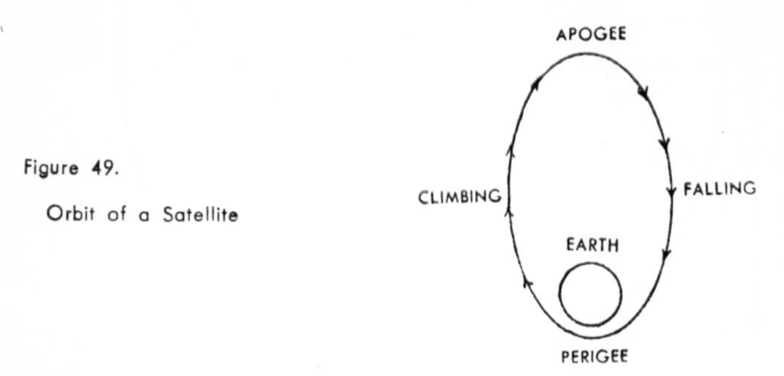

Figure 49.
Orbit of a Satellite

In orbit, the satellite travels an elliptical path around the Earth. At its closest point, the satellite is said to be in "perigee" and at its farthest point, it is in "apogee." See Figure 49. The orbit is usually calculated so that at perigee the satellite does not enter the Earth's atmosphere. The slowing up of the satellite due to the frictional drag of the Earth's atmosphere will change its orbital pattern and eventually pull it back to Earth.

The angle at which the satellite is launched is important in determining what area of the Earth's surface will be covered by the orbit. The greater the angle of inclination of launching, the greater will be the area covered by the orbiting satellite. Figure 50 shows the area covered by a launching whose angle of inclination to the Earth's equator is 60°. Such an angle will allow the orbit to cover an area from Alaska, in the north, to the tip of South America, in the south. The first Sputnik was launched in approximately this orbit. The angle of most

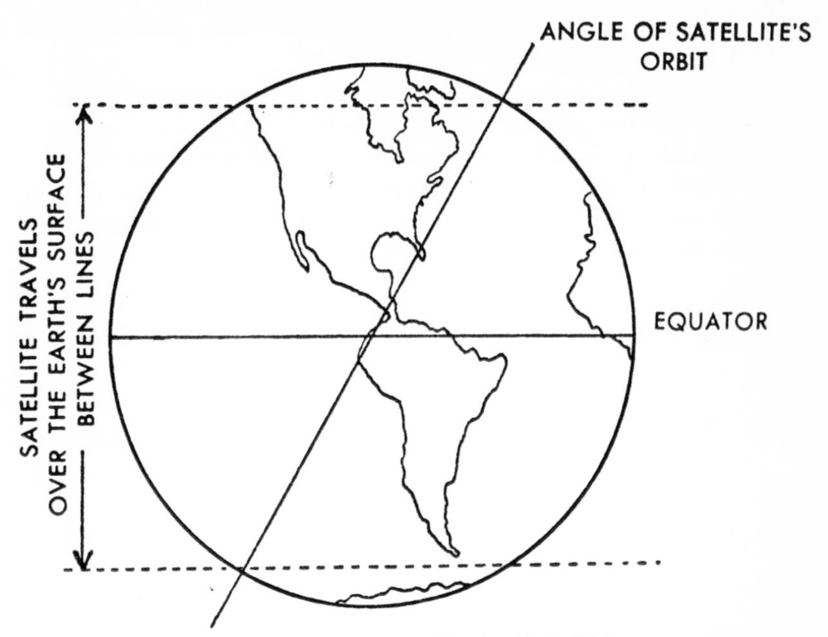

Figure 50. Inclination Of a Satellite's Orbit

satellite launches is from 40° to 60° of inclination from the equator.

Operation Moonwatch

The sky-watcher who wishes to track satellites is well-advised to join a "Moonwatch" team. These small groups, using low power, wide field telescopes, cover specific areas of the sky along the predicted orbit of the satellite. They time the passage of the satellite in their particular area of the sky and submit the data to the group headquarters. This method has had great value in helping to confirm the speed and direction of the orbits of the different satellites.

Working as an individual, the sky-watcher will have a more difficult time in tracking satellites. Information as to orbits and the time of the satellite's "passes" must be obtained from published newspaper reports, which may, or may not be, accurate. Fortunately, the astronomical publications print, from time to time, more detailed information on current satellites.

Widefield telescopes, or properly mounted high power binoculars, are best when searching the skies for the faint, luminous streak that marks the passage of a satellite.

APPENDIX I

CHARTS AND TABLES OF DATA

Work Program Of Observations For Beginners

Note: The schedule outlined below is intended as a general guide for beginners. Whether it can be followed, or not, depends, in part, on available time, existing conditions for observing, time of year, etc. It should be considered as a flexible timetable.

I. Preliminary Steps

- A. Learn techniques of assembling and disassembling telescope.
- B. Become familiar with movement of the telescope mounting and "slow motions".
- C. Examine and determine uses of all accessories.

II. First Observations (Daylight)

- A. Make terrestrial observations to become familiar with focusing, use of star diagonal, image erecter, different eyepieces, etc.
- B. Adjust viewfinder telescope for proper alignment with main telescope. (See page 40)

III. First Night Observations

- A. Observing the Moon.
  1. Look for dark "seas", craters (Tycho and Copernicus).
  2. Observe area of the terminator (See page 65)
- B. Constellation study. Particular attention to circumpolar stars. (See page 108)

IV. Second Night Observations

- A. Planetary obserationvs.
  1. Jupiter: Observe banded atmosphere, Great Red Spot, four main moons. (See page 83)

2. Saturn: Observe ring system, Cassini's Division (See page 86).

B. Constellation study. Familiarization with constellations of the current month.

V. Third Night Observations

A. Star clusters (open clusters).

1. The Pleiades
2. The Hyades

(See page 110, 111, 119)

B. Constellation study. Learn the visible constellations of the Zodiac. (See page 75)

VI. Fourth Night Observations

A. Double Stars

1. Albireo in Constellation of Cygnus.
2. Castor in Constellation of Gemini (See page 118).

B. Constellation study. Become familiar with constellation boundaries.

VII. Fifth Night Observations

A. Double Stars

1. Antares in Constellation of Scorpio.
2. Trapezium (quadruple star) in Constellation of Orion.

B. Constellation study. Check position of minor constellations.

VIII. Sixth Night Observations

A. Nebulae (extra galactic)

1. Great Spiral in Andromeda — Messier 31.
2. Spiral in Ursa Major — Messier 81 (See page 128)

IX. Seventh Night Observations

A. Nebulae (diffuse)

1. "Lagoon" nebula in Sagittarius — Messier 8.
2. Nebula in Orion — Messier 42 (See page 124).

Telescope Accessories

Name of Accessory	Description and Use
Star diagonal	Prismatic device permitting viewer to see at right angles to telescope tube. Rotates to any position for comfortable viewing. Will accommodate any eyepiece.
Erecting prism	Re-inverts the normally inverted image of the telescope and reverses it to provide images which are identical with actuality. Indispensable for land observations.
Erecting lens	Provides the same effect as the erecting prism, but functions by means of lenses rather than prisms.
Sun lens (filter)	A dark filter of heat-resistant glass. Screws into eyepiece to protect eyes when making direct observations of the Sun.
Lunar lens (filter)	A tinted glass filter for use when viewing the Moon during periods of maximum brightness. Lunar lens fits into eyepiece and reduces glare, while increasing contrast.
Barlow lens	Magnifying system used with standard eyepieces to increase magnification power of available eyepieces. Increases power by 2X or 3X.
Sun diagonal	A right-angle observing device which materially reduces the amount of light reaching the observer when viewing the Sun directly. A valuable safety device.

Sun projection screen — A screen with bracket that can be clamped to telescope to permit projection of Sun's image on to screen. Excellent for indirect observation of Sun. Can be seen by group of observers and permits drawing of projected sunspots with ease.

Sun diaphragm — An adjustable diaphragm which is placed before the objective to control amount of light when photographing the Sun.

Camera bracket holder — Clamp-type bracket which holds camera in proper position for astro-photography. Can be adjusted to various heights for different cameras.

Extra eyepieces — Eyepieces vary in the magnification they provide. Different kinds are used in situations that require varied performance. Eyepieces can greatly increase the versatility of any instrument.

Clock drives — Mechanical device designed to move or drive the telescope at same rate that stars appear to travel. Keeps a star in view automatically. Electric motor, spring wound, or weight-driven models are available.

TABLE OF THE CONSTELLATIONS

Name	Latin Genitive	English Name	Culmination
Andromeda	Andromedae	Lady In Chains	Oct. 9
Antlia	Antliae	The Pump	Feb. 24
Apus	Apodis	The Bee	May 21
Aquarius	Aquarii	Water Bearer	Aug. 25
Aquila	Aquilae	The Eagle	Jul. 16
Ara	Arae	The Altar	Jun. 10
Aries	Arietis	The Ram	Oct. 30
Auriga	Aurigae	The Charioteer	Dec. 21
Boötes	Boötis	The Herdsman	May 2
Caelum	Caeli	The Sculptor's Tools	Dec. 1
Camelopardus	Camelopardi	The Giraffe	Dec. 23
Cancer	Cancri	The Crab	Jan. 30
Canes Venatici	Canem Venaticorum	The Hunting Dogs	Apr. 7
Canis Major	Canis Majoris	The Big Dog	Jan. 2
Canis Minor	Canis Minoris	The Little Dog	Jan. 14
Capricornus	Capricorni	The Goat	Aug. 8
Carina	Carinae	The Ship's Keel	Jan. 31
Cassiopeia	Cassopeiae	Queen In The Chair	Oct. 9
Centaurus	Centauri	The Centaur	Mar. 30
Cepheus	Cephei	The King	Sep. 29
Cetus	Ceti	The Whale	Oct. 15
Chamaeleon	Chamaeleontis	The Chameleon	Mar. 1
Circinus	Circini	The Compasses	Apr. 30
Columba	Columbae	The Dove	Dec. 18
Coma Berenices	Comae Berenices	Berenice's Hair	Apr. 2
Corona Australis	Coronae Australis	The Southern Crown	Jun. 30
Corona Borealis	Coronae Borealis	The Northern Crown	May 18
Corvus	Corvi	The Crow	Mar. 28
Crater	Crateris	The Cup	Mar. 12
Crux	Crucis	The Southern Cross	Mar. 28
Cygnus	Cvgni	The Swan	Jul. 30
Delphinus	Delphini	The Dolphin	Jul. 31
Dorado	Doradus	The Swordfish	Dec. 17
Draco	Draconis	The Dragon	May 24
Equuleus	Equulei	The Little Horse	Aug. 8
Eridanus	Eridani	The River	Nov. 10
Fornax	Fornacis	The Furnace	Nov 2
Gemini	Geminorum	The Twins	Jan. 5
Grus	Gruis	The Crane	Aug. 28
Hercules	Herculis	Hercules	Jun. 13
Horologium	Horologii	The Clock	Nov. 10
Hydra	Hydrae	The Sea Serpent	Mar. 15
Hydrus	Hydri	The Water Snake	Oct. 26
Indus	Indi	The Indian	Aug. 12
Lacerta	Lacertae	The Lizard	Aug. 28
Leo	Leonis	The Lion	Mar. 1
Leo Minor	Leonis Minoris	The Little Lion	Feb. 23

TABLE OF THE CONSTELLATIONS

Name	Latin Genitive	English Name	Culmination
Lepus	Leporis	The Hare	Dec. 14
Libra	Librae	The Scales	May 9
Lupus	Lupi	The Wolf	May 9
Lynx	Lyncis	The Lynx	Jan. 19
Lyra	Lyrae	The Harp	Jul. 4
Mensa	Mensae	The Table	Dec. 14
Microscopium	Microscopii	The Microscope	Aug. 4
Monoceros	Monocerotis	The Unicorn	Jan. 5
Musca	Muscae	The Fly	Mar 30
Norma	Normae	The Ruler	May 19
Octans	Octantis	The Octant	Circumpolar S.
Ophiuchus	Ophiuchi	Serpent Holder	Jun. 11
Orion	Orionis	The Hunter	Dec. 13
Pavo	Pavonis	The Peacock	Jul. 15
Pegasus	Pegasi	The Winged Horse	Sep. 1
Perseus	Persei	Slayer of Medusa	Nov. 7
Phoenix	Phoenicis	The Phoenix	Oct. 4
Pictor	Pictoris	The Painter	Dec. 16
Pisces	Piscium	The Fishes	Sep. 27
Piscis Austrinus	Piscis Austrini	The Southern Fish	Aug. 25
Puppis	Puppis	The Ship's Poop	Jan. 8
Pyxis	Pyxidis	Mariner's Compass	Feb. 4
Reticulum	Reticuli	The Net	Nov 19
Sagitta	Sagittae	The Arrow	Jul. 16
Sagittarius	Sagittarii	The Archer	Jul. 7
Scorpius	Scorpii	The Scorpion	Jun. 3
Sculptor	Sculptoris	The Sculptor	Sep. 26
Scutum	Scuti	The Shield	Jul. 1
Serpens	Serpentis	The Serpent	Jun. 6
Sextans	Sextantis	The Sextant	Feb. 22
Taurus	Tauri	The Bull	Nov. 30
Telescopium	Telescopii	The Telescope	Jul. 10
Triangulum	Trianguli	The Triangle	Oct. 23
Triangulum Australis	Trianguli Australis	The Southern Triangle	May 23
Tucana	Tucanae	The Toucan	Sep. 17
Ursa Major	Ursae Majoris	The Big Bear (Dipper)	Mar. 11
Ursa Minor	Ursae Minoris	The Little Bear (Dipper)	May 13
Vela	Velorum	The Ship's Sails	Feb. 13
Virgo	Virginis	The Virgin	Apr 11
Volans	Volantis	The Flying Fish	Jan. 18
Vulpecula	Vulpeculae	The Fox	Jul. 25

Culmination: The date at which the constellation reaches the highest point above the observer's horizon. The culmination will be reached at *midnight* of the date recorded.

MESSIER'S CATALOGUE OF NEBULAE & STAR CLUSTERS

Messier No.	Type	Constellation
1	Nebula (Crab Nebula)	Taurus
2	Globular Cluster	Aquarius
3	Globular Cluster	Canes Venatici
4	Globular Cluster	Scorpius
5	Globular Cluster	Serpens
6	Open Cluster	Scorpius
7	Open Cluster	Scorpius
8	Nebula (Lagoon Nebula)	Sagittarius
9	Globular Cluster	Ophiuchus
10	Globular Cluster	Ophiuchus
11	Open Cluster	Scutum
12	Globular Cluster	Ophiuchus
13	Globular (Great Cluster)	Hercules
14	Globular Cluster	Ophiuchus
15	Globular Cluster	Pegasus
16	Open Cluster	Serpens
17	Nebula (Horseshoe Nebula)	Sagittarius
18	Open Cluster	Sagittarius
19	Globular Cluster	Ophiuchus
20	Nebula (Trifid Nebula)	Sagittarius
21	Open Cluster	Sagittarius
22	Globular Cluster	Sagittarius
23	Open Cluster	Sagittarius
24	Open Cluster	Sagittarius
25	Open Cluster	Sagittarius
26	Open Cluster	Scutum
27	Nebula (Dumbbell Nebula)	Vulpecula
28	Globular Cluster	Sagittarius
29	Open Cluster	Cygnus
30	Globular Cluster	Capricornus
31	Great Spiral Galaxy	Andromeda
32	Satellite Galaxy of M 31	Andromeda
33	Spiral Galaxy	Triangulum
34	Open Cluster	Perseus
35	Open Cluster	Gemini
36	Open Cluster	Auriga
37	Open Cluster	Auriga
38	Open Cluster	Auriga
39	Open Cluster	Cygnus
40	(Not identified)	
41	Open Cluster	Canis Major
42	Great Nebula	Orion
43	Nebula	Orion
44	Open Cluster (Praesepe)	Cancer
45	Open Cluster (Pleiades)	Taurus
46	Open Cluster	Puppis
47	Open Cluster	Puppis
48	Open Cluster	Hydra
49	Elliptical Galaxy	Virgo
50	Open Cluster	Monoceros
51	Whirlpool Galaxy	Canes Venatici
52	Open Cluster	Cassiopeia
53	Globular Cluster	Coma Berenice's
54	Globular Cluster	Sagittarius
55	Globular Cluster	Sagittarius

MESSIER'S CATALOGUE OF NEBULAE & STAR CLUSTERS

Messier No.	Type	Constellation
56	Globular Cluster	Lyra
57	Ring Nebula	Lyra
58	Spiral Galaxy	Virgo
59	Elliptical Galaxy	Virgo
60	Elliptical Galaxy	Virgo
61	Spiral Galaxy	Virgo
62	Globular Cluster	Ophiuchus
63	Spiral Galaxy	Canes Venatici
64	Spiral Galaxy	Coma Berenices
65	Spiral Galaxy	Leo
66	Spiral Galaxy	Leo
67	Open Cluster	Cancer
68	Globular Cluster	Hydra
69	Globular Cluster	Sagittarius
70	Globular Cluster	Sagittarius
71	Globular Cluster	Sagitta
72	Globular Cluster	Aquarius
73	Open Cluster	Aquarius
74	Spiral Galaxy	Pisces
75	Globular Cluster	Sagittarius
76	Planetary Nebula	Perseus
77	Spiral Galaxy	Cetus
78	Nebula	Orion
79	Globular Cluster	Lepus
80	Globular Cluster	Scorpius
81	Great Spiral Galaxy	Ursa Major
82	Irregular Galaxy	Ursa Major
83	Spiral Galaxy	Hydra
84	Elliptical Galaxy	Virgo
85	Spiral Galaxy	Coma Berenices
86	Elliptical Galaxy	Virgo
87	Elliptical Galaxy	Virgo
88	Spiral Galaxy	Coma Berenices
89	Elliptical Galaxy	Virgo
90	Spiral Galaxy	Virgo
91	(Not identified)	
92	Globular Cluster	Hercules
93	Open Cluster	Puppis
94	Spiral Galaxy	Canes Venatici
95	Spiral Galaxy	Leo
96	Spiral Galaxy	Leo
97	Owl Nebula	Ursa Major
98	Spiral Galaxy	Coma Berenices
99	Spiral Galaxy	Coma Berenices
100	Spiral Galaxy	Coma Berenices
101	Spiral Galaxy	Ursa Major
102	Spiral Galaxy	Draco
103	Open Cluster	Cassiopeia
104	Spiral Galaxy	Virgo
105	Spiral Galaxy	Leo
106	Spiral Galaxy	Canes Venatici
107	Globular Cluster	Ophiuchus

Note: The objects listed are visible from the area of latitude 40° North. All are readily found with small telescopes.

TABLE FOR THE CONVERSION OF STANDARD TIME TO UNIVERSAL TIME

Universal Time	Eastern Standard Time	Central Standard Time	Mountain Standard Time	Pacific Standard Time
0h	7 P.M.	6 P.M.	5 P.M.	4 P.M.
1	8	7	6	5
2	9	8	7	6
3	10	9	8	7
4	11	10	9	8
5	12 midnight	11	10	9
6	1 A.M.	12 midnight	11	10
7	2	1 A.M.	12 midnight	11
8	3	2	1 A.M.	12 midnight
9	4	3	2	1 A.M.
10	5	4	3	2
11	6	5	4	3
12	7	6	5	4
13	8	7	6	5
14	9	8	7	6
15	10	9	8	7
16	11	10	9	8
17	12 noon	11	10	9
18	1 P.M.	12 noon	11	10
19	2	1 P.M.	12 noon	11
20	3	2	1 P.M.	12 noon
21	4	3	2	1 P.M.
22	5	4	3	2
23	6	5	4	3

THE BRIGHTEST STARS

Name of Star	Location		Apparent Magnitude
	R.A.	Dec.	
Sirius	6h 43m	−16° 38′	−1.58
Canopus	6 22	−52 40	−0.86
Vega	18 35	+38 44	0.14
Capella	5 12	+45 58	0.21
Arcturus	14 13	+19 28	0.24
Rigel	5 12	− 8 15	0.34
Procyon	7 36	+ 5 22	0.48
Achernar	1 35	−57 30	0.60
Altair	19 48	+ 8 43	0.89
Betelgeuse	5 52	+ 7 24	0.92
Aldebaran	4 33	+16 25	1.06
Pollux	7 42	+28 9	1.21
Spica	13 22	−10 54	1.21
Antares	16 26	−26 20	1.22
Fomalhaut	22 54	−29 53	1.29
Deneb	20 39	+45 6	1.33
Regulus	10 57	+12 13	1.34
Castor	7 31	+32 0	1.58

TABLE OF IMPORTANT METEOR SHOWERS

Date	Shower	Constellation	Radiant		Remarks
			R.A.	Dec.	
Feb. 5	Aurigids	Auriga	5h 20m	+41°	slow, often fireballs
April 20	Lyrids	Lyra	18 4	+33	fast, thin streaks
May 6	Aquarids	Aquarius	22 16	− 2	very fast
June 2	Scorpiids	Scorpius	16 52	−22	slow, fireballs
Aug. 10	Perseids	Perseus	3 0	+57	very fast, streaky
Aug. 21	Draconids	Draco	19 24	+60	slow, bright
Oct. 18	Orionids	Orion	6 8	+15	fast, streaks
Nov. 13	Leonids	Leo	10 0	+22	big display 1966
Nov. 17	Andromedids	Andromeda	1 40	+43	Biela's Comet remains
Dec. 10	Geminids	Gemini	7 28	+33	many, bright

TABLE OF MODERN NOVAE

First Observed	Designation	Position				Greatest Magnitude
		R.A.		Dec.		
1600	Cygni No. 1	20h	16m	+37°	52′	3.5
1670	Vulpeculae	19	46	+27	11	3
1866	Coronae	15	57	+26	4	2
1887	Persei No. 1	1	58	+56	29	9.2
1901	Persei No. 2	3	26	+43	24	0.0
1910	Lacertae No. 1	22	33	+52	22	5.5
1918	Aquilae No. 3	18	46	+ 0	32	−0.7
1919	Lyrae	18	51	+29	9	6.5
1920	Cygni No. 3	19	57	+53	29	1.8
1934	Herculis	18	7	+45	51	1.3
1942	Puppis	8	10	−35	13	0.4
1950	Lacertae	22	48	+53	2	6.0

A TABLE OF PERIODIC COMETS

Year of Discovery	Name of Comet	Period of Recurrence in Years
1806	Biela's Comet (not extant)	6.7
1812	Di Vico's Comet	70.7
1819	Encke's Comet	3.3
1835	Halley's Comet	76.3
1871	Tuttle's Comet	13.8
1879	Brorsen's Comet	5.6
1889	Swift II	7.0
1923	d'Arrest's Comet	6.6
1925	Schwassmann-Wachmann Comet	16.2
1956	Arend-Roland Comet	—

TOTAL SOLAR ECLIPSES

Date	Area Where Visible
May 20, 1966	Mediterranean Sea, Atlantic Ocean
November 12,1966	South America, Indian Ocean
November 2, 1967	Antarctica
September 22, 1968	Northern Russia to Central Asia
March 7, 1970	Florida, Mexico
July 10, 1972	Northern Canada, Alaska
June 30, 1973	South America, Atlantic Ocean
June 20, 1974	Indian Ocean, Antarctic Ocean
October 23, 1976	East Africa, Australia
October 12, 1977	Northern South America
February 26, 1979	Northwest United States
February 16, 1980	Central Africa, India, China
July 31, 1981	Southeastern Europe
June 11, 1983	East Indies
May 30, 1984	Southern United States, Mexico
November 22, 1984	East Indies, Chile
November 12, 1985	Antarctic Ocean
October 3, 1986	Greenland
March 29, 1987	Africa, South Atlantic Ocean
March 18, 1988	Philippine Islands
July 22, 1990	Finland, Arctic Ocean
July 11, 1991	Mexico, Central America
June 30, 1992	South America
November 3, 1994	South America

A TABLE OF PLANET LOCATIONS

(Positions In Band Of Zodiac)

	VENUS	MARS	JUPITER	SATURN
1965 Jan	Sagittarius	Virgo-Leo	Aries	Aquarius
1965 Feb	*	Virgo-Leo	Aries	Aquarius
1965 Mar	*	Leo	Taurus-Aries	Aquarius
1965 Apr	*	Leo	Taurus	Aquarius
1965 May	*	Leo	Taurus	Aquarius
1965 Jun	Evening Star	Virgo-Leo	Taurus	Aquarius-Pisces
1965 Jul	Leo-Cancer	Virgo	Taurus	Aquarius-Pisces
1965 Aug	Virgo-Leo	Virgo	Taurus	Aquarius
1965 Sep	Virgo	Libra	Gemini-Taurus	Aquarius
1965 Oct	Scorpius	Scorpius	Gemini-Taurus	Aquarius
1965 Nov	Sagittarius	Sagittarius	Gemini-Taurus	Aquarius
1965 Dec	Capricornus	Sagittarius	Gemini-Taurus	Aquarius
1966 Jan	Morning Star	Capricornus	Taurus	Aquarius
1966 Feb	Capr-Sagitt	Aquarius	Taurus	Aquarius
1966 Mar	Capricornus	Pisces	Taurus	Pisces-Aquarius
1966 Apr	Aquarius	Aries-Pisces	Gemini-Taurus	Pisces
1966 May	Pisces	Aries	Gemini-Taurus	Pisces
1966 Jun	Aries	Taurus	Gemini	Pisces
1966 Jul	Taurus	Gemini-Taurus	Gemini	Pisces
1966 Aug	Cancer-Gemini	Cancer-Gemini	Gemini	Pisces
1966 Sep	*	Cancer	Cancer-Gemini	Pisces
1966 Oct	*	Leo	Cancer	Pisces-Aquarius
1966 Nov	*	Leo	Cancer	Pisces-Aquarius
1966 Dec	*	Virgo	Cancer	Pisces-Aquarius
1967 Jan	Evening Star	Virgo	Cancer	Pisces
1967 Feb	Pisc-Aquarius	Virgo	Cancer-Gemini	Pisces
1967 Mar	Pisces	Libra-Virgo	Cancer-Gemini	Pisces
1967 Apr	Taurus	Virgo	Cancer-Gemini	Pisces
1967 May	Gemini	Virgo	Cancer-Gemini	Pisces
1967 Jun	Cancer	Virgo	Cancer	Pisces
1967 Jul	Leo	Virgo	Cancer	Pisces
1967 Aug	Leo	Libra	Leo-Cancer	Pisces
1967 Sep	Morning Star	Scorpius	Leo	Pisces
1967 Oct	Leo	Sagit-Scorpius	Leo	Pisces
1967 Nov	Virgo	Sagittarius	Leo	Pisces
1967 Dec	Libra-Virgo	Capricornus	Leo	Pisces
1968 Jan	Scorpius	Aquarius	Leo	Pisces
1968 Feb	Sagittarius	Pisces	Leo	Pisces
1968 Mar	Aquar-Capric	Pisces	Leo	Pisces
1968 Apr	*	Aries	Leo	Pisces
1968 May	*	Taurus	Leo	Pisces
1968 Jun	*	Taurus	Leo	Pisces
1968 Jul	*	Gemini	Leo	Aries-Pisces
1968 Aug	Evening Star	Cancer	Leo	Aries-Pisces
1968 Sep	Virgo	Leo	Leo	Aries-Pisces
1968 Oct	Libra	Leo	Virgo-Leo	Pisces
1968 Nov	Sagitt-Scorp	Virgo	Virgo	Pisces
1968 Dec	Capricornus	Virgo	Virgo	Pisces
1969 Jan	Aquarius	Libra-Virgo	Virgo	Pisces
1969 Feb	Pisces	Scorpius-Libra	Virgo	Pisces
1969 Mar	Aries-Pisces	Scorpius	Virgo	Aries-Pisces
1969 Apr	Morning Star	Scorpius	Virgo-Leo	Aries-Pisces
1969 May	Pisces	Scorpius	Virgo-Leo	Aries
1969 Jun	Aries	Scorpius	Virgo-Leo	Aries
1969 Jul	Taurus	Scorpius	Virgo	Aries
1969 Aug	Gemini	Scorpius	Virgo	Aries
1969 Sep	Leo-Cancer	Sagitt-Scorp	Virgo	Aries
1969 Oct	Virgo-leo	Sagittarius	Virgo	Aries
1969 Nov	*	Capricornus	Virgo	Aries
1969 Dec	*	Aquarius-Capr	Virgo	Aries
1970 Jan	*	Pisces-Aquarius	Libra-Virgo	Aries
1970 Feb	*	Pisces	Libra-Virgo	Aries
1970 Mar	Evening Star	Aries	Libra-Virgo	Aries
1970 Apr	Aries	Aries-Taurus	Virgo	Aries
1970 May	Taurus	Taurus	Virgo	Aries
1970 Jun	Cancer-Gemini	Gemini	Virgo	Aries
1970 Jul	Leo-Virgo	Cancer-Gemini	Virgo	Taurus-Aries
1970 Aug	Virgo	Leo-Cancer	Virgo	Taurus-Aries
1970 Sep	Libra-Virgo	Leo	Libra-Virgo	Taurus-Aries
1970 Oct	Libra	Virgo-Leo	Libra	Taurus-Aries
1970 Nov	Morning Star	Virgo	Libra	Aries
1970 Dec	Libra	Libra-Virgo	Libra	Aries

* **Note:** Venus in line with the Sun and not readily observable.

A TABLE OF PLANETARY DATA

	Mercury	Venus	Earth	Mars	Jupiter	Saturn	Uranus	Neptune	Pluto
Distance from Sun (Millions of Miles)	36	67.3	93	142	484	887	1784	2795	3675
Period of Revolution Around Sun	88d	224d	365d	1.8^y	11.8^y	29.5^y	84^y	165^y	248.4^y
Period of Rotation on Axis	88d	?	24h	24h	9h 50m	10h 14m	10h 45m	15.8h	?
Diameter (Miles)	3,000	7,575	7,926	4,215	88,700	75,060	30,878	27,700	3,600
Number of Satellites	0	0	1	2	12	9	5	2	0
Maximum Magnitude	−1.2	−4.4	......	−2.8	−2.5	−0.4	5.7	7.8	14
Surface Gravity	0.28	0.85	1.0	0.38	2.6	1.1	0.9	1.1	?
Inclination of Equator (Degrees)	7	?	23.4	25.2	3.1	26.8	98	29	?

Note: d = days, y = years, h = hours, m = minutes

STATISTICS OF PLANETARY SATELLITES

Name	Diameter	Magnitude	Distance From Planet	Sidereal Period	
Earth					
Moon	2160 miles	– 12.5	238,000 miles	27 days	7 hrs
Mars					
Phobos	10	10	5,800	0	7½
Deimos	5	11	14,600	1	6
Jupiter					
Io	2310	5.5	262,000	1	18
Europa	1950	5.7	417,000	3	13
Ganymede	3200	5.1	666,000	7	3
Callisto	3220	6.3	1,170,000	16	16
(V)	150	13	113,000	0	12
(VI)	100	13.7	7,120,000	250	16
(VII)	35	17	7,290,000	259	16
(VIII)	35	16	14,600,000	739	
(IX)	17	18.6	14,700,000	758	
(X)	15	18.8	7,300,000	260	12
(XI)	19	18.4	14,000,000	700	
(XII)	14	18.9	13,000,000	625	
Saturn					
Mimas	300	12.1	113,000	0	22½
Enceladus	400	11.6	149,000	1	9
Tethys	800	10.6	183,000	1	21
Dione	1000	10.7	235,000	2	17½
Rhea	1100	9.7	328,000	4	12½
Titan	3500	8.2	760,000	15	22½
Hyperion	200	13.0	920,000	21	6½
Iapetus	2000	9.0	2,200,000	79	8
Phoebe	150	14.0	8,050,000	550	11
Uranus					
Miranda	200	17.0	76,000	1	10
Ariel	1500	14.0	119,000	2	12½
Umbriel	800	14.7	166,000	4	3½
Titania	1500	14.0	272,000	8	17
Oberon	1500	14.0	364,000	13	11
Neptune					
Triton	3300	13.0	220,000	5	21
Nereid	200	19.5	3,500,000	359	

A TABLE OF INTERESTING DOUBLE STARS

Designation	Location		Characteristics
	R.A.	Dec.	
Beta Cygni	19h 28m	+27°51′	Yellow and Blue. Fine Contrast
Gamma Delphini...	20 44	+15 57	Green and Yellow
Epsilon Lyrae	18 42	+39 37	The "double-double"
Alpha Scorpii	16 26	−26 20	Red and Green (Antares)
Alpha Herculis......	17 12	+14 27	Orange and Green
Gamma Virginis ...	12 39	− 1 10	Excellent Binary Pair
Iota Cancri	8 43	+28 57	Yellow and Blue. Good Contrast
Alpha Geminorum	7 31	+32 0	Fine double. (Castor)
Eta Persei............	2 47	+55 41	Smaller companions. Fine colors
Gamma Arietis ...	1 50	+19 3	Fine pair in small telescope
Alpha Piscium......	1 59	+ 2 31	Blue and Pale Green. Test 2-inch
Alpha Lyrae.........	18 35	+38 44	Vega. An optical double
Psi Draconis.........	17 43	+72 12	Purple and Yellow
Mu Librae	14 46	−13 57	Test for 2½-inch telescope
Alpha Tauri.........	4 33	+16 25	Fine Pair (Aldebaran)
Epsilon Bootis	14 42	+27 17	Yellow and Blue. 2-inch test

A TABLE OF VARIABLE STARS

Designation	Type	Period	Location	
			R.A.	Dec.
Delta Cephei ...	Short-period Cepheid	5.37 days	22h 27m	+58° 10′
Omicron Ceti ...	(Mira) Long-period variable	331 days	2 16	− 3 12
Beta Persei	(Algol) Binary Eclipsing Variable	2.87 days	3 5	+38 39
Lambda Tauri...	Algol Type	3.9 days	3 57	+12 20
Beta Lyrae	Typical Lyrid. Bright-eclipsing variable	12.9 days	18 48	+33 18
Chi Cygni	Long-period variable	409 days	19 48	+32 48
Epsilon Aurigae .	Spectroscopic binary	27.1 years	4 58	+43 44
Alpha Orionis ...	(Betelgeuse) Irregular variable	....	5 52	+ 7 24
Zeta Geminorum	Cepheid variable	10.2 days	7 1	+20 39
Delta Librae......	Algol Type	2.33 days	14 58	− 8 19

A TABLE OF NEBULAE AND STAR CLUSTERS

Designation	Constellation	Description	Location	
			R.A.	Dec.
NGC 6543	Draconis	Planetary nebula. Bluish oval disc.	17h 58m	+66° 38′
Messier 81	Ursae Majoris	Bright spiral with faint arms.	9 51	+69 18
Messier 31	Andromedae	The "Great Nebula" spiral. Long oval.	0 40	+41 0
Messier 38	Aurigae	Loose, cruciform star cluster.	5 25	+35 48
Messier 42	Orionis	Great nebula of Orion. Fan-shaped, greenish mass.	5 32	− 5 25
Messier 44	Cancri	"Bee-hive" cluster. Large, scattered with orange stars.	8 37	+20 10
NGC 2244	Monocerotis	Open cluster with large yellow star.	6 30	+ 4 54
Messier 97	Ursae Majoris	"Owl" nebula, large faint planetary.	11 11	+55 17
Messier 13	Herculis	"Great Cluster" huge globular cluster.	16 39	+36 33
Messier 7	Scorpii	Brilliant open cluster.	17 50	−34 48
Messier 57	Lyrae	"Ring Nebula" oval planetary.	18 52	+32 58
Messier 17	Sagittarii	"Horseshoe" nebula large and bright.	18 18	−16 12
NGC 5139	Centauri	Superb globular, like a tailless comet.	13 23	−47 3
NGC 884	Persei	Fine paired clusters with ruby star in center.	2 17	+56 55
NGC 7243	Lacertae	Open irregular cluster. Fine object.	22 13	+49 38

TABLE OF ASTRONOMICAL SIGNS AND SYMBOLS

Sun	☉
Mercury	☿
Venus	♀
Earth	⊕
Moon	☽
Mars	♂
Jupiter	♃
Saturn	♄
Uranus	♅
Neptune	♆
Pluto	♇
Conjunction	☌
Opposition	☍
Quadrature	□
1st of Aries	♈
Ascending	☊
Descending	☋

TOTAL LUNAR ECLIPSES

Date	Area Where Visible
April 24, 1967	Pacific Ocean, Australia
October 18, 1967	Western North America
April 12, 1968	United States, Mexico, South America
October 6, 1968	Australia
February 10, 1971	United States, Southern Canada
August 6, 1971	Africa, India
January 30, 1972	Western North America
November 29, 1974	Australia, Asia
May 25, 1975	Southern United States, Mexico
November 18, 1975	Europe, Africa
March 24, 1978	Australia, Asia
September 16, 1978	Southern Asia, Africa
September 6, 1979	Australia
January 9, 1982	Eastern Europe
July 6, 1982	Mexico, South America
December 30, 1982	Pacific Ocean

NUMBER OF STARS

The number of stars in the sky classified according to magnitude. For stars of magnitude less than 5, the figures given are approximate.

Magnitude	Number Of Stars
Brighter than magnitude 1.0	12
Magnitude 1.0 to 2.0	28
Magnitude 2.0 to 3.0	103
Magnitude 3.0 to 4.0	315
Magnitude 4.0 to 5.0	1,050
Magnitude 5.0 to 6.0	3,300
Magnitude 6.0 to 7.0	17,000
Magnitude 7.0 to 8.0	50,000
Magnitude 8.0 to 9.0	150,000
Magnitude 9.0 to 10.0	500,000
Magnitude 10.0 to 11.0	1,650,000
Magnitude 11.0 to 12.0	3,700,000
Magnitude 12.0 to 13.0	7,650,000
Magnitude 13.0 to 14.0	16,000,000

ANGULAR DISTANCE BETWEEN CERTAIN STARS

The angular distances given below for selected stars are useful in computing approximate angular measurement between heavenly bodies.

Approximate Degrees	Selected Stars Of Known Angular Measure
2	From Altair to Gamma Aquilae
4.5	From Castor to Pollux
5	From Alpha Ursa Majoris to Merak
10	From Betelgeuse to Mintaka
15	From Alpheratz to Mirach
20	From Procyon to Pollux
25	From Sirius to Procyon
30	From Aldebaran to Capella
35	From Vega to Altair
40	From Regulus to Castor
45	From Deneb to Polaris
50	From Castor to Sirius
60	From Dubhe to Caph

SOME STANDARD MAGNITUDE STARS

(For Comparison and Estimation of Stars)

Approximate Magnitude	Name Of Star	Actual Magnitude
– 1.5	Sirius	– 1.44
0	Vega	0.00
+ 0.5	Achernar	0.60
+ 1.0	Spica	0.98
+ 1.5	Castor	1.58
+ 2.0	Polaris	2.12
+ 2.5	Gamma Ursa Majoris	2.54
+ 3.0	Beta Draconis	2.99
+ 3.5	Epsilon Cassiopeiae	3.44
+ 4.0	Delta Cancri	4.17
+ 4.5	Psi Ursa Majoris	4.54
+ 5.0	Eta Ursa Minoris	5.04

TABLE OF STARS CLOSEST TO EARTH

Name Of Star	Distance In Light-Years	Apparent Magnitude
Alpha Centauri A	4.3	0.3
Alpha Centauri B	4.3	1.7
Sirius	8.6	– 1.6
Epsilon Eridani	10.7	3.8
Procyon	11.0	0.5
61 Cygni	11.1	5.6
Epsilon Indi	11.2	4.7
Tau Ceti	11.2	3.6
Altair	15.7	0.9

A TABLE OF STAR NAMES

Common Name	Bayer System Name
Achernar	Alpha Eridani
Albireo	Beta Cygni
Alcor	80 Ursae Majoris
Aldebaran	Alpha Tauri
Alioth	Epsilon Ursae Majoris
Alphard	Alpha Hydrae
Alphecca	Alpha Coronae Borealis
Alpheratz	Alpha Andromedae
Altair	Alpha Aquilae
Antares	Alpha Scorpii
Arcturus	Alpha Bootis
Bellatrix	Gamma Orionis
Betelgeuse	Alpha Orionis
Canopus	Alpha Carinae
Capella	Alpha Aurigae
Caph	Beta Cassiopeiae
Castor	Alpha Geminorum
Deneb	Alpha Cygni
Denebola	Beta Leonis
Dubhe	Alpha Ursae Majoris
El Nath	Beta Tauri
Fomalhaut	Alpha Piscis Austrini
Gemma	Alpha Coronae Borealis
Kochab	Beta Ursae Minoris
Megrez	Delta Ursae Majoris
Menkar	Alpha Ceti
Merak	Beta Ursae Majoris
Mintaka	Delta Orionis
Mira	Omicron Ceti
Mirzam	Beta Canis Majoris
Phad	Gamma Ursae Majoris
Polaris	Alpha Ursae Majoris
Procyon	Alpha Canis Majoris
Regulus	Alpha Leonis
Rigel	Beta Orionis
Sadal Melik	Alpha Aquarii
Saiph	Kappa Orionis
Sirius	Alpha Canis Majoris
Spica	Alpha Virginis
Thuban	Alpha Draconis
Vega	Alpha Lyrae
Zavijava	Beta Virginis
Zubenelgenubi	Alpha Librae

APPENDIX II

CONSTELLATION MAPS FOR THE STELLAR YEAR

The Stellar Year

The following constellation charts depict the sky for every month of the year. This is the Northern Sky as visible to an observer at latitudes of 40° North. This is the parallel of latitude that, more or less, divides the United States into an upper and lower half. It runs through Philadelphia, Indianapolis, Denver, and Northern California. For a distance of 8° on either side of this parallel, the star maps will be, in essence, correct. The area defined covers most of the United States from Mexico to Canada.

No attempt has been made to indicate all of the constellations that are visible for each month. However, the key constellations and the major stars have been included. Constellation outlines are merely diagramatic and are intended only as a guide to the main stars in a group.

The symbol ✱ has been used for the bright stars of the first magnitude and greater. These sixteen bright stars of the Northern Sky range from Sirius (magnitude —1.58) to Castor (magnitude 1.6). Reference should be made to the main chart of constellations, in the pocket on the rear cover, for specific information as to star names, location of celestial objects and other information.

The observer should make every effort to become familiar with the constellations and the main stars as they complete their yearly circle around the celestial pole. A few nights each month spent studying the constellations that are current will soon find the observer "at home among the stars."

NOTES FOR THE JANUARY SKY

The constellations of the January sky are dominated by the group of magnificent southern constellations that ride high in the heavens at this time of year. Brilliant Orion leads the parade, and points the way to Sirius, the brightest star in the heavens.

This is a good month to observe the rich star fields in Orion. Looking in the area south of the Belt, the observer will see several faint stars and a hazy, blur of light. The nebulous patch is the "Great Nebula." It is in the nebula that the Trapezium (Theta Orionis), the quadruple star may be seen. One of the marks of competence in the amateur astronomer is to "split" the Trapezium.

Almost directly overhead in the expanse of the January sky is the collection of faint stars that form Perseus. Of chief interest here, is the star, Beta Persei, which is the famous eclipsing binary variable, Algol.

Taurus, easily found by its red, first magnitude star, Aldebaran, is a fine object in the January sky. The open cluster of the Pleiades, forming the shoulder of Taurus, the Bull, is a sparkling sight at low powers.

Sirius and Procyon, the main stars of the Big and Little Dog, are well placed for observation. They are two of the brightest stars in the southern sky and have been used as navigation stars by generations of seamen.

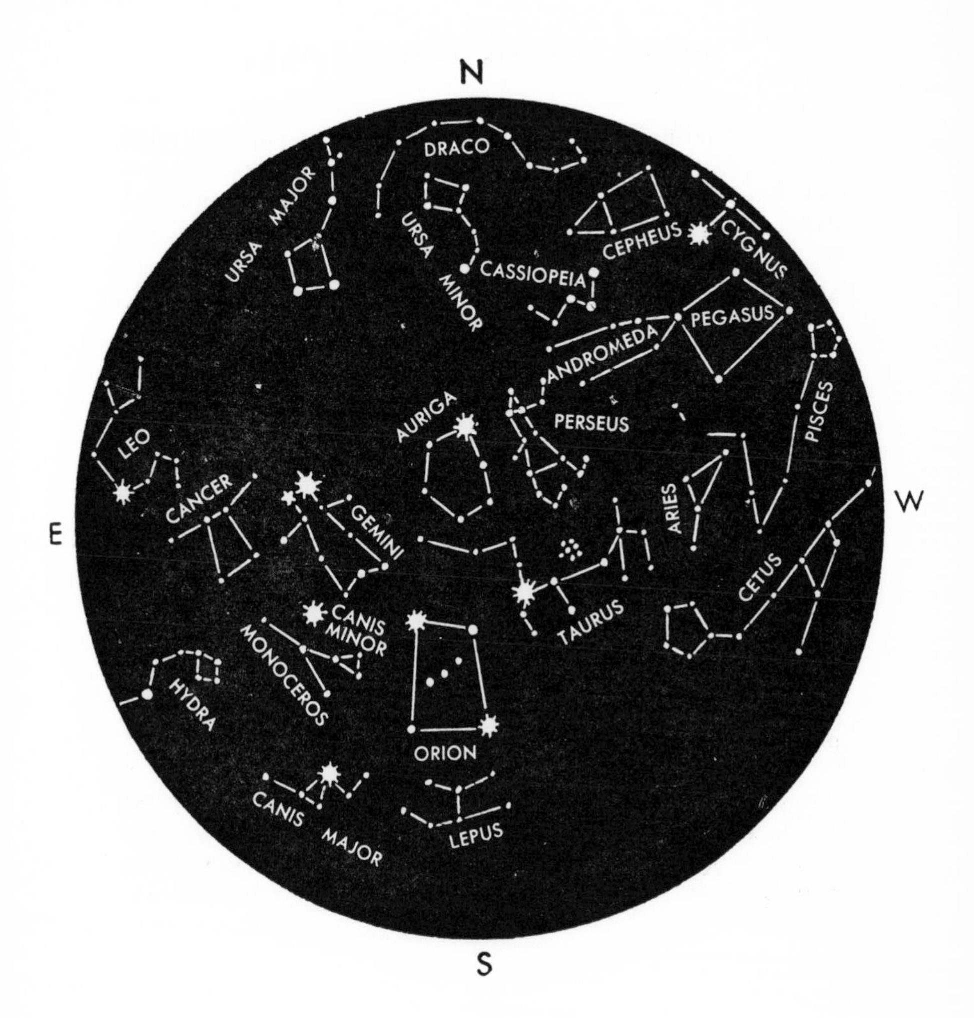

THE JANUARY SKY

NOTES FOR THE FEBRUARY SKY

Almost directly overhead, a clearly drawn pentagon of stars forms a setting for the brilliant Capella. This is the constellation, Auriga. Capella is one of the five brightest stars in the sky. Calculations have shown that Capella is moving away from the Earth at fantastic speeds: about 68,400 miles per hour. In one night Capella has drawn 1,631,300 miles farther away.

In February, both of the great constellations of the Northern Sky are almost equally prominent: The Big Dipper and Orion. The Dipper with its pointer stars leads the eye to Polaris — the site of the North Celestial Pole. This is a good time to test a three-inch telescope by trying to "split" Polaris, which has a dim companion of the ninth magnitude.

The clear, cold February nights lend a brilliance to the sky that is unsurpassed at any time of the year. The amateur will be well repaid if he attempts some star-gazing in this coldest month. A telescope is not really necessary as medium powered binoculars will serve to pick up the major star groups.

The starting point for February observations is directly overhead. Four bright stars serve to lead the eye to the constellations that are in the ascendancy. The stars are Aldebaran, Capella, and the Twins: Castor and Pollux.

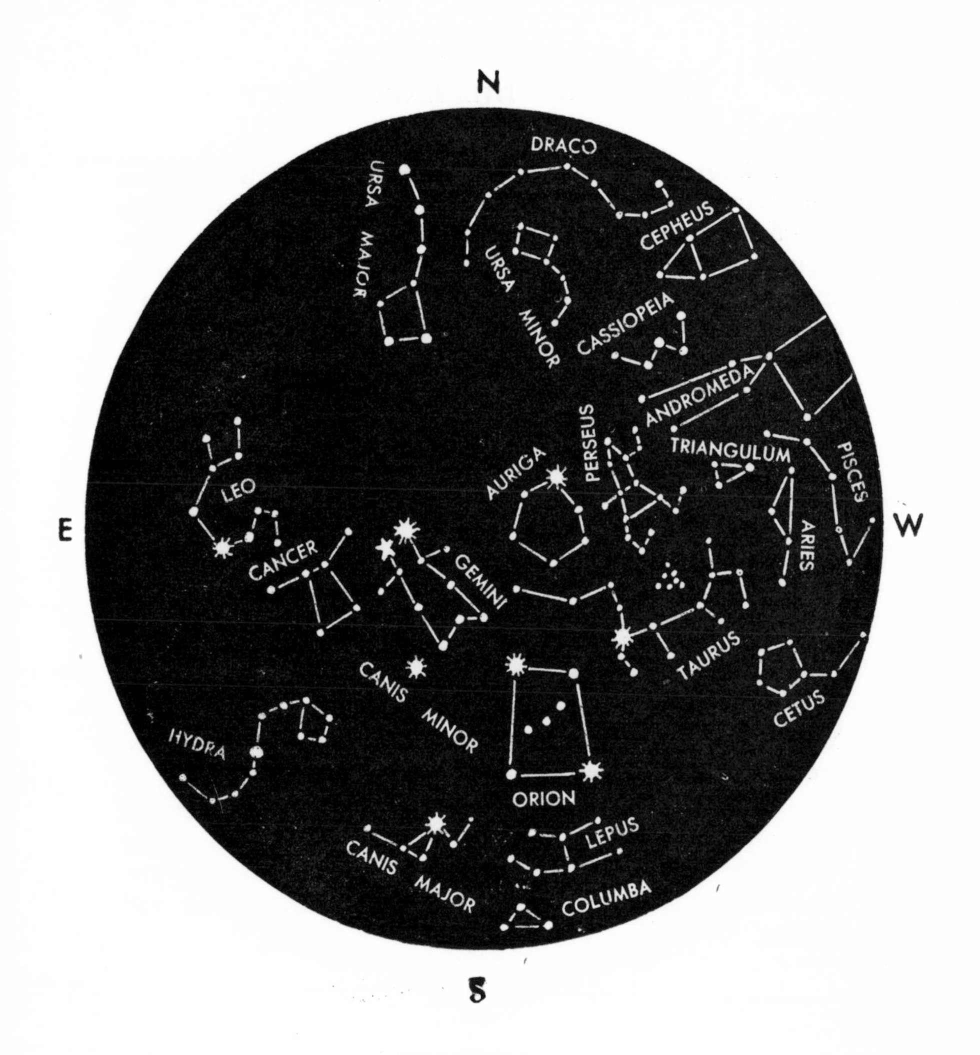

THE FEBRUARY SKY

NOTES FOR THE MARCH SKY

A fine constellation for study in March is Gemini, the Twins. Gemini is one of the star groups that make up the constellations of the Zodiac. The name, the Twins, derives from the presence of two bright stars which are quite close together, Castor and Pollux. At least, they appear to be very close. Actually they form something of an optical double, lying, as they do, along the same line of sight.

In the constellation of Gemini, will be found a handsome star cluster, Messier 35. In the small telescope, the cluster and a pair of trailing streams of stars form a beautiful object for study. It is well worth observing.

Castor is a multiple star. It has two companions and it is possible to achieve some resolution of this multiple star in telescopes of moderate size. Recent investigation indicates that each of the stars in the system is probably a double, which makes Castor a six star system.

Sirius and Procyon, which are also well placed in the March sky, are both multiple stars, but their companions are too dim to be seen with ordinary telescopes.

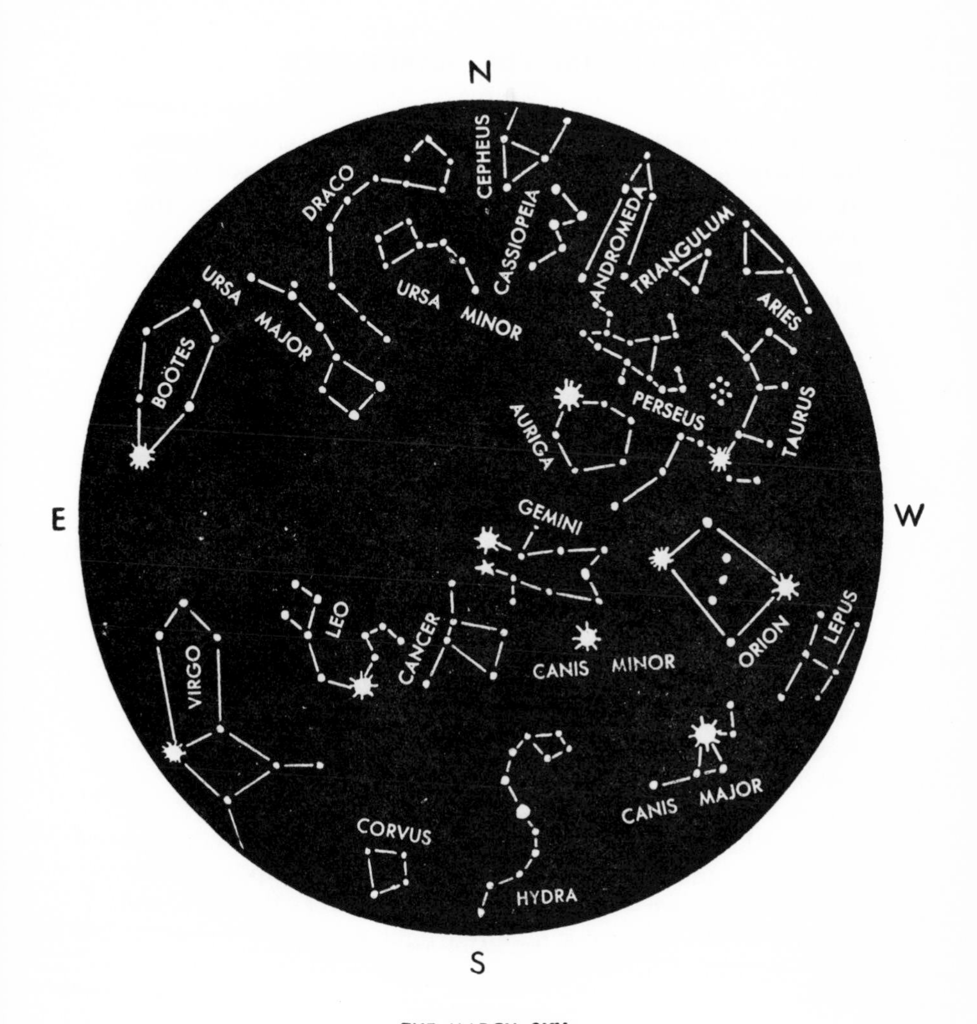

THE MARCH SKY

NOTES FOR THE APRIL SKY

The constellation of Leo, with its bright star, Regulus, lies close to the zenith in this month. The constellation is often recognized by looking for its "sickle" shape. Regulus lies in the "handle" of the sickle.

A fine double star is to be seen in the constellation of Leo. Gamma Leonis is a beautifully contrasting double, with the main star having a gold color and the companion, a greenish glow. This double system, incidentally, is rushing toward the Earth at about 24 miles per *second.* From one night to the next it has approached the Earth by some two million miles. However, the immense distances that separate us from Gamma Leonis cannot be spanned, even at these speeds, in the course of many, many centuries.

The constellation of the Northern Crown, the Corona Borealis is a feature of the April sky. There are seven stars in the "crown" arranged in an almost perfect circlet. The constellation makes a lovely sight in the field of high-powered binoculars. The middle star in the circlet has been named Alphecca — the Pearl of the Crown. The whole "crown" is really a beautiful arrangement of stars.

Although it is one of the smallest of the constellations in appearance, the Corona Borealis takes up a goodly amount of space — the actual distance across the open end of the circlet is over a hundred light years.

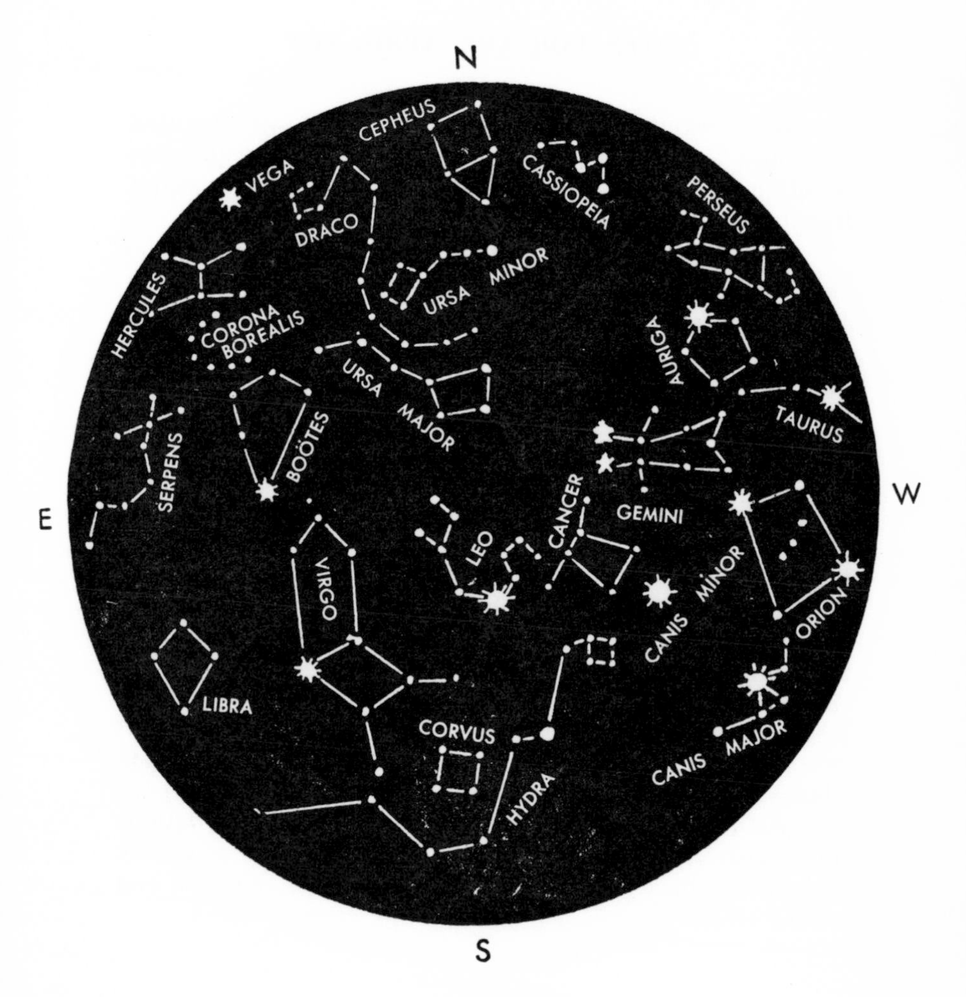

THE APRIL SKY

NOTES FOR THE MAY SKY

Rising in the eastern part of the heavens, are two important constellations: Hercules and Lyra. They will move higher and higher in the sky now as the year grows older.

Hercules is the site of the "Great Cluster." This globular cluster may well be the greatest collection of stars in the entire sky. It can be seen as a filmy patch of light on a line drawn between Arcturus and Vega. Only high-powered telescopes can resolve the patch into the fantastic aggregation of stars that make up this brilliant cluster.

The brightest star in the constellation, Alpha Herculis is one of the largest stars known. It is about 700 million miles in diameter. It is also a double star that is easily resolved in small binoculars.

Lyra is noted for its chief star, Vega, which is one of the brightest stars in the sky. It is a double star with an orange-colored companion that is much dimmer. In the constellation, Lyra, we also find the "double-double", Epsilon Lyrae.

In Lyra, also, may be found the "Ring Nebula", which appears much like a misty smoke ring. It is listed as Messier 57, and a three-inch telescope will begin to reveal its curious ring shape.

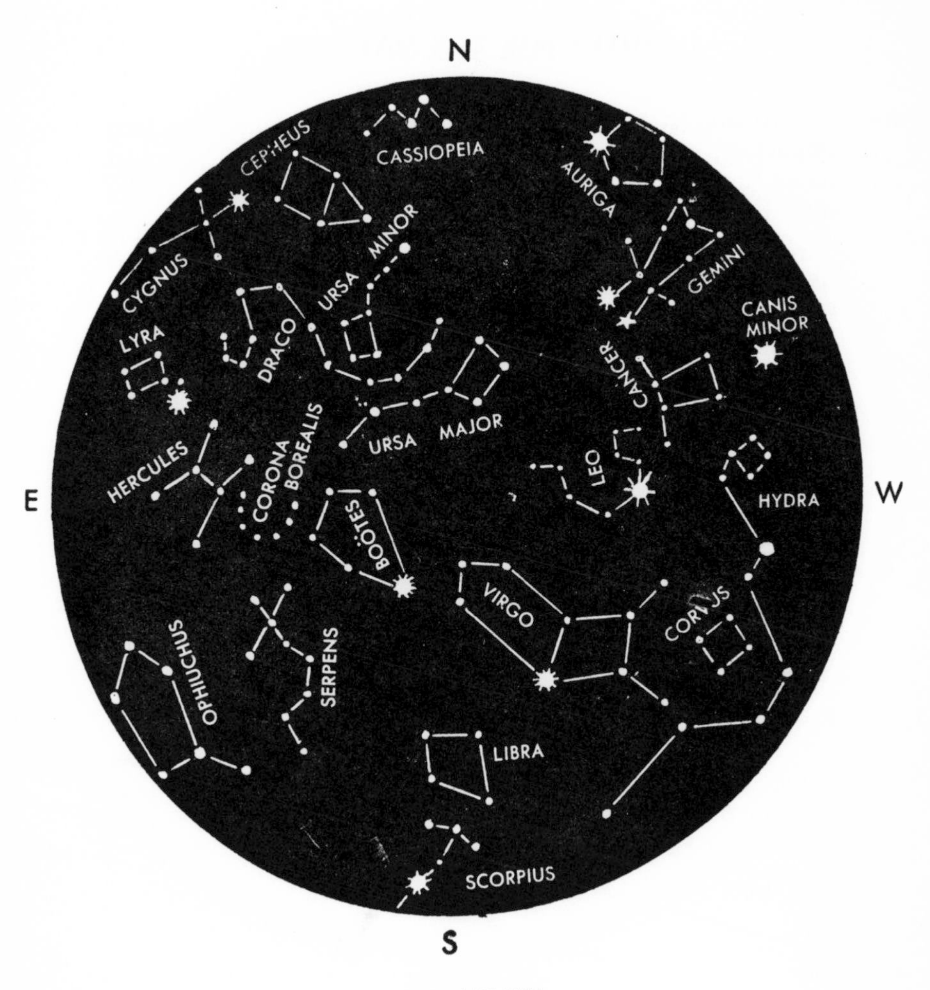
N
E
W
S
CASSIOPEIA
CEPHEUS
AURIGA
CYGNUS
URSA MINOR
GEMINI
CANIS MINOR
LYRA
DRACO
CANCER
URSA MAJOR
HERCULES
CORONA BOREALIS
LEO
HYDRA
BOÖTES
VIRGO
SERPENS
OPHIUCHUS
LIBRA
SCORPIUS

THE MAY SKY

NOTES FOR THE JUNE SKY

Boötes and Virgo are the constellations which occupy the zenith at this time of year. Both are very interesting star groups.

Boötes is the constellation of the bright, reddish star, Arcturus, which is the fourth brightest star visible from these latitudes. Boötes contains many double stars, the most beautiful of which is Epsilon Boötis. The color contrast of this double, gold and green, is noteworthy. Xi Boötis is a double which boasts a yellow and purple color combination.

Virgo is the constellation that points to the nebulae. Looking upward from Spica, in the arms of the "Y", will be found a telescope field especially rich in nebulae. This region of the sky is called The Field of the Nebulae.

Virgo also boasts a fine double. This is Gamma Virginis, a true binary. The period of this binary is about 180 years and the two components are of similar color and brightness.

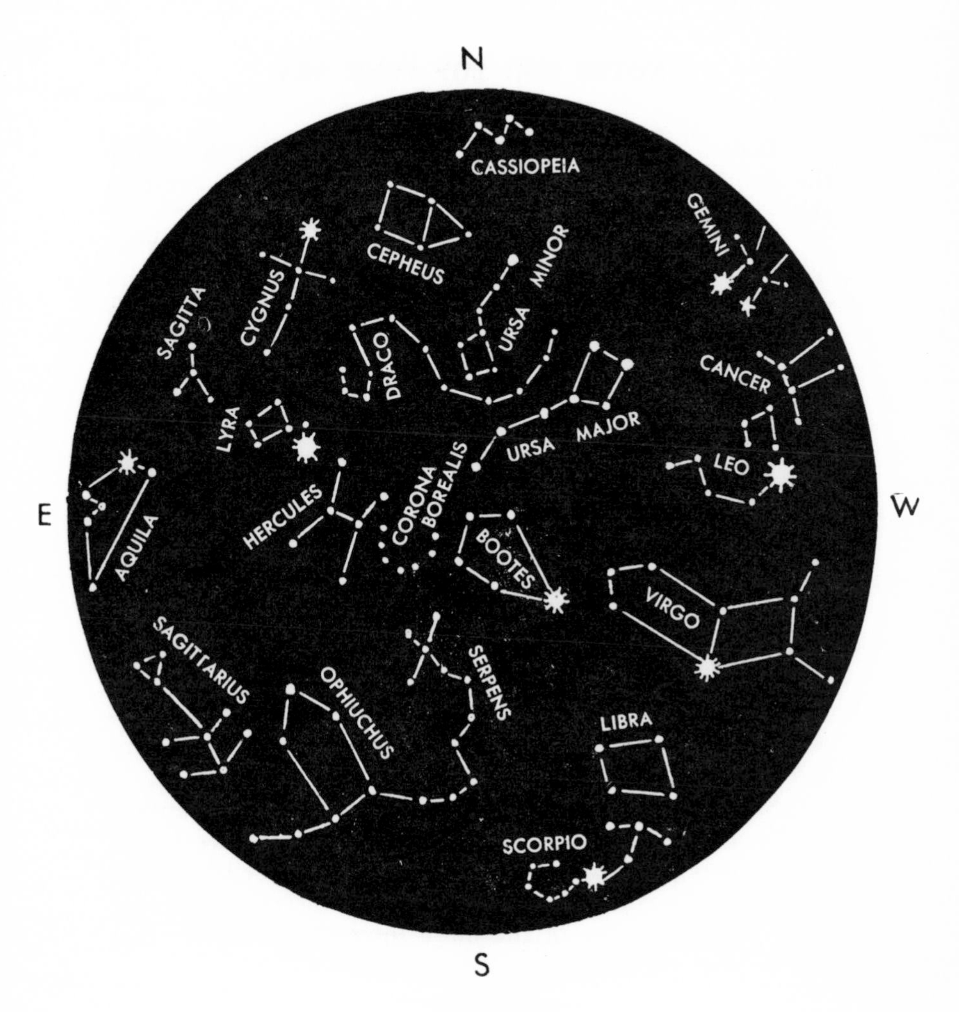
N
CASSIOPEIA
CEPHEUS
GEMINI
URSA MINOR
CYGNUS
SAGITTA
DRACO
CANCER
LYRA
URSA MAJOR
LEO
CORONA BOREALIS
HERCULES
E
W
AQUILA
BOOTES
VIRGO
SAGITTARIUS
SERPENS
OPHIUCHUS
LIBRA
SCORPIO
S

THE JUNE SKY

NOTES FOR THE JULY SKY

The constellation of the Scorpion visits our skies during this month. Scorpius lies below the celestial equator and for much of the year cannot be seen above the horizon by the sky-watcher at 40° North latitude. On turning his gaze southward, the observer will be rewarded by the sight of this sharply defined constellation marked by the great red star Antares.

Larger than our Sun by 350 times, Antares is a good example of a relatively "cool" red giant star; its surface temperature is about 5,500° F. This monster star is actually a double with a smaller and dimmer companion that exhibits a marked greenish hue. A four-inch telescope is required to resolve this double as the two stars are separated by only about three seconds of arc.

Another fine double in Scorpius, however, can be resolved in more modest telescopes. The star, Beta Scorpii makes an appealing contrast with its yellow and green components.

Lying between Antares and Beta Scorpii is the interesting star cluster, Messier 80. It is a rich globular composed of thousands of stars.

Sagittarius is a constellation that is seen to advantage during July. It does not contain any bright stars but it defines a region that is noted for its many brilliant star clusters. The constellation chart in the insert on the rear cover indicates some of the more interesting clusters that can be studied with a small telescope.

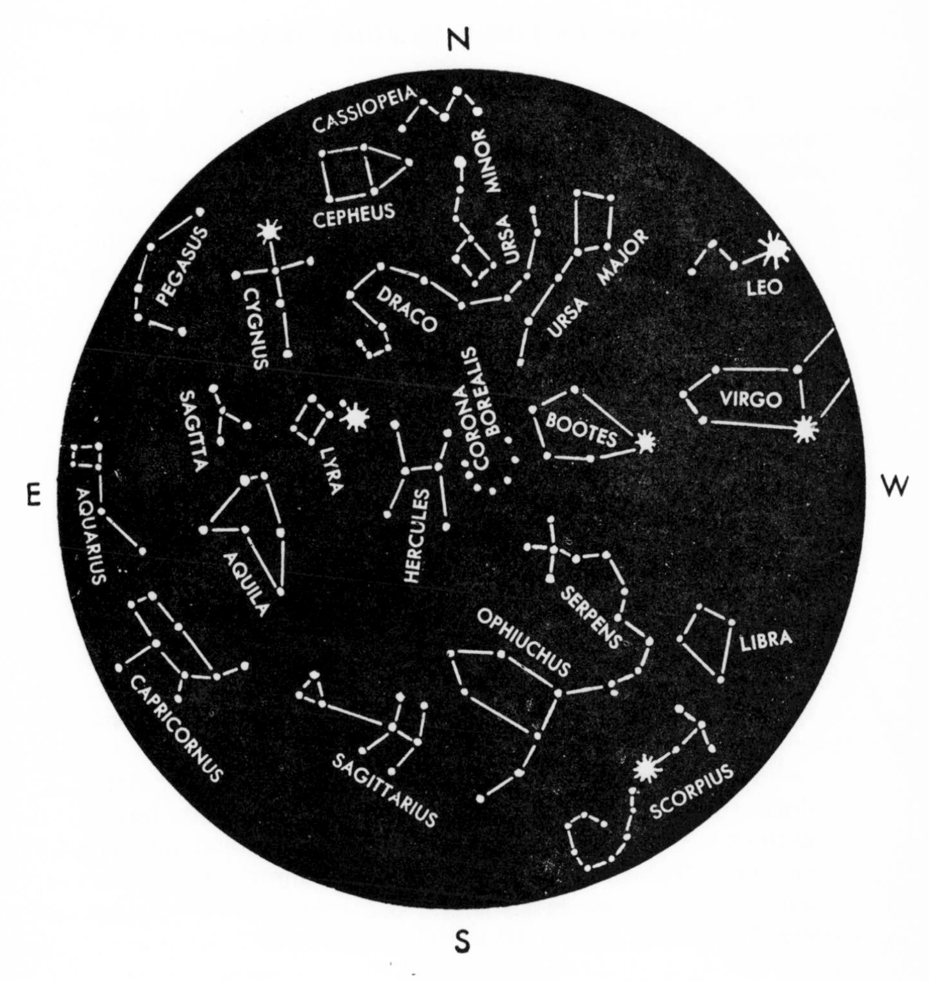
N
E
W
S
CASSIOPEIA
CEPHEUS
URSA MINOR
PEGASUS
CYGNUS
DRACO
URSA MAJOR
LEO
CORONA BOREALIS
VIRGO
SAGITTA
LYRA
BOOTES
AQUARIUS
AQUILA
HERCULES
SERPENS
OPHIUCHUS
LIBRA
CAPRICORNUS
SAGITTARIUS
SCORPIUS

THE JULY SKY

NOTES FOR THE AUGUST SKY

The summer constellations are well displayed in the August sky, ranging from the Big Dipper in the north to Scorpius in the south. Towards the northeast, the double line of stars that mark the outline of Andromeda may be readily seen.

Andromeda is the home of the Great Spiral Nebula, the distant galaxy of a billion stars. In telescopes of low power, this spiral-armed galaxy may be seen as a bright, egg-shaped blur. All attempts to focus this filmy patch sharply will fail as it is not a single point of light like a star; it is, instead, the diffused light of a billion suns spanning incredible distances.

The constellation of Andromeda leads the eye to the Great Square of Pegasus. The star, Alpheratz is not only part of the Andromeda constellation, but it forms one of the corners of the Great Square. Both constellations share this star.

A double star affording a fine study in contrasts is to be seen in Pegasus. The star is Epsilon Pegasi. The brighter component is golden yellow while the companion star is of a distinctly purple coloration. Telescopes of moderate power are needed to split this double.

South of Andromeda lies the minor constellation of Triangulum. It is in Triangulum that the Earth's closest neighboring galaxy is to be found. The foggy blur, that is called Messier 33, is an island universe like our own, the Milky Way. This neighbor is but 750,000 light years away which is about as close as another universe can get without crowding.

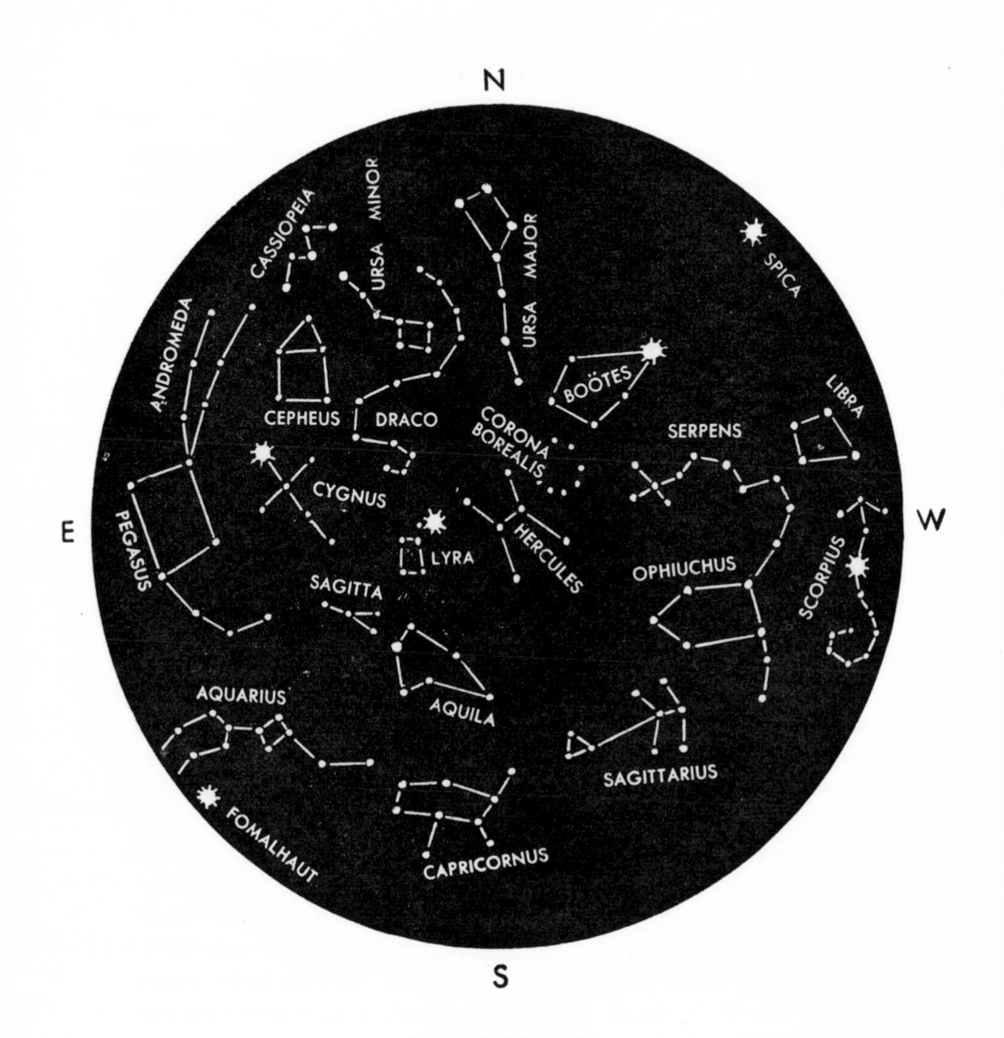

THE AUGUST SKY

NOTES FOR THE SEPTEMBER SKY

Cygnus, sometimes called the Northern Cross, dominates the zenith at this time of year. The bright star at the head of the "cross" is Deneb, one of the beacon stars of the northern sky; it is only slightly dimmer than a first magnitude star.

The Milky Way, like a great river of stars, splits into two parallel streams at the constellation of Cygnus. The observer who studies this portion of the sky will find it rich in beautiful star clusters and nebulae.

At the opposite end of the long arm of the "cross" from Deneb, a telescope of low power will resolve what is probably the most beautiful double star in the heavens. The star is the famed Albireo, Beta Cygni. It is an easy double to split and the finely contrasted yellow and blue pair will provide a real thrill when first viewed in the telescope. The stars are of the third and fifth magnitudes.

Directly below Deneb to the south, another bright first magnitude star shines forth from near the zenith. It is Altair, the shining jewel in the constellation of Aquila. The telescope will show Altair to be a double star with a rather dim companion of the tenth magnitude. This star, incidentally, is a very close neightbor of ours; it is "only" 14 light years away from Earth.

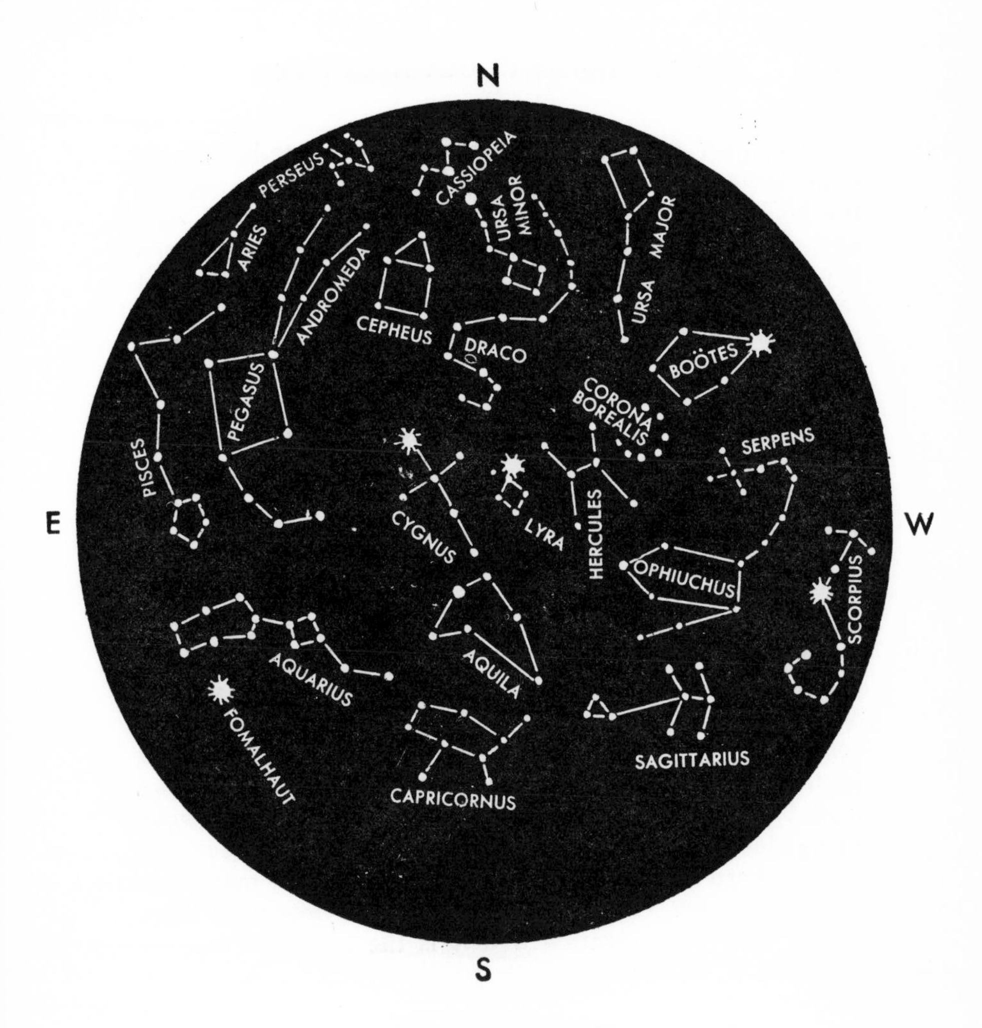

THE SEPTEMBER SKY

NOTES FOR THE OCTOBER SKY

Cepheus, one of the circumpolar constellations, is noteworthy principally because of the presence of the star Delta Cephei. This is a double star, easily split with a small telescope. However, this is not its claim to fame. The brighter component is a variable star of the type that has given its name to many stars of a similar nature scattered throughout the universe. It is the prototype of all the Cepheid variables.

Delta Cephei varies in magnitude from a minimum of 4.6 to a maximum of 3.7. The time required for this variation in brightness to occur is exactly 5 days, 8 hours, 47 minutes, and 39 seconds.

The constellation Cepheus merits our attention in another way; it is the setting for the reddest star in the heavens. Mu Cephei, known as the Garnet Star, can be readily observed at low powers of the telescope.

A bright, bluish star gleams in solitary majesty in the southern sky during the autumn months. This serene, first-magnitude star is Fomalhaut, sometimes called the Lonely One. It forms part of the constellation of Piscis Austrinus, and as it rises in the southern sky its grandeur is undimmed as there are few bright stars to be found in its vicinity. The star is said to "lie in the mouth of the Southern Fish" and this is exactly what is meant by its Arabic name. Fomalhaut is one of the important stars that is used in navigation and it is the brightest star on the southern horizon.

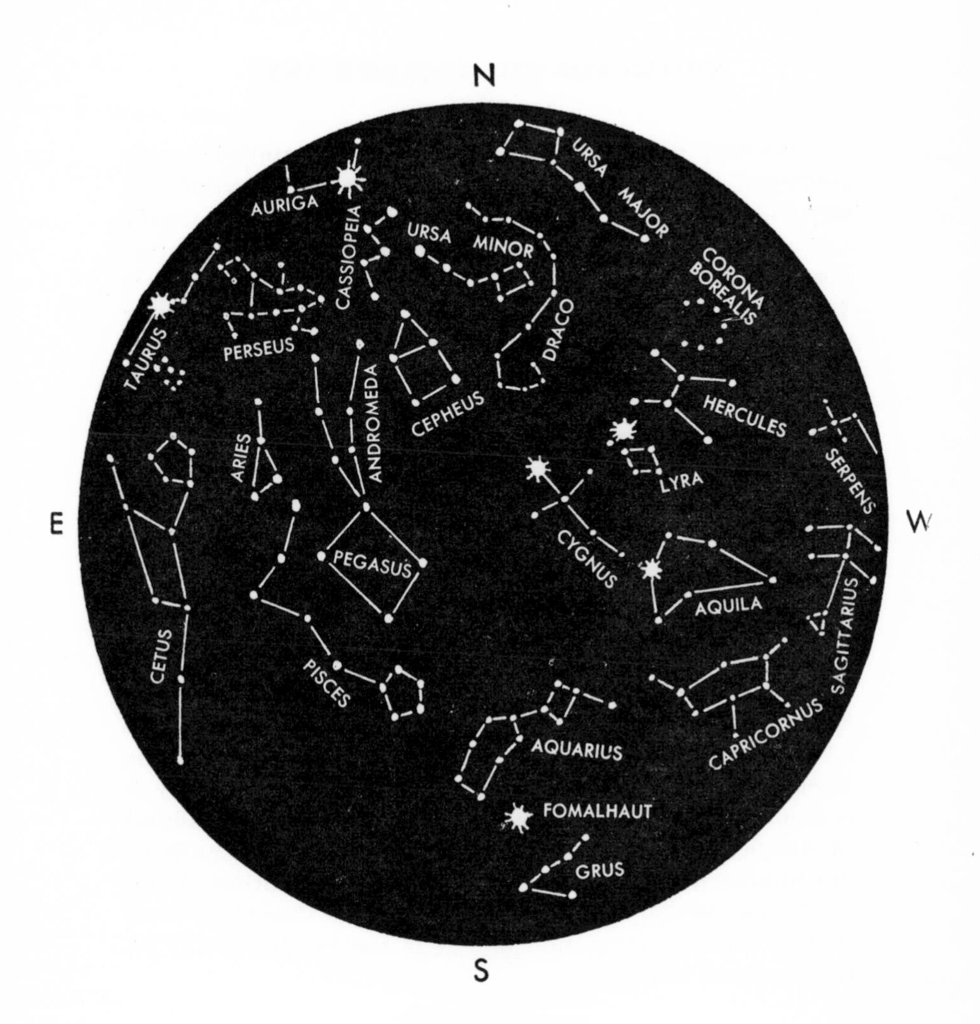

THE OCTOBER SKY

NOTES FOR THE NOVEMBER SKY

At this time of year, the familiar circumpolar constellation of Cassiopeia lies as close to the zenith as it will approach. It is a fertile field for telescope study and many fine star clusters and double stars populate this area of the sky. The brightest star in the group that forms this "W" in the sky, Alpha Cassiopeiae, is a double that can be resolved without difficulty in small telescopes. Another star, Sigma Cassiopeiae, is a lovely double with components that are blue and green, a fine contrast. The field of the sky near Sigma Cassiopeiae is magnificent at low power. Particularly noteworthy is the nearby star cluster, NGC 7789 which has been described by many observers as one of the finest of its type.

In the southern sky a great, sprawling constellation is traced by a group of relatively dim stars — the constellation of the Whale. Here may be found the notable star Mira, or Omicron Ceti, the "Wonderful Star." It is the prototype of the long-period variables, with a change in magnitude from a bright third-magnitude star to one of the tenth magnitude, invisible to the naked eye. The period of variability is irregular; an average period is about one year. Studies are constantly being made of this star in the hope that it will reveal some of the clues leading to a broader knowledge of the evolution of our universe.

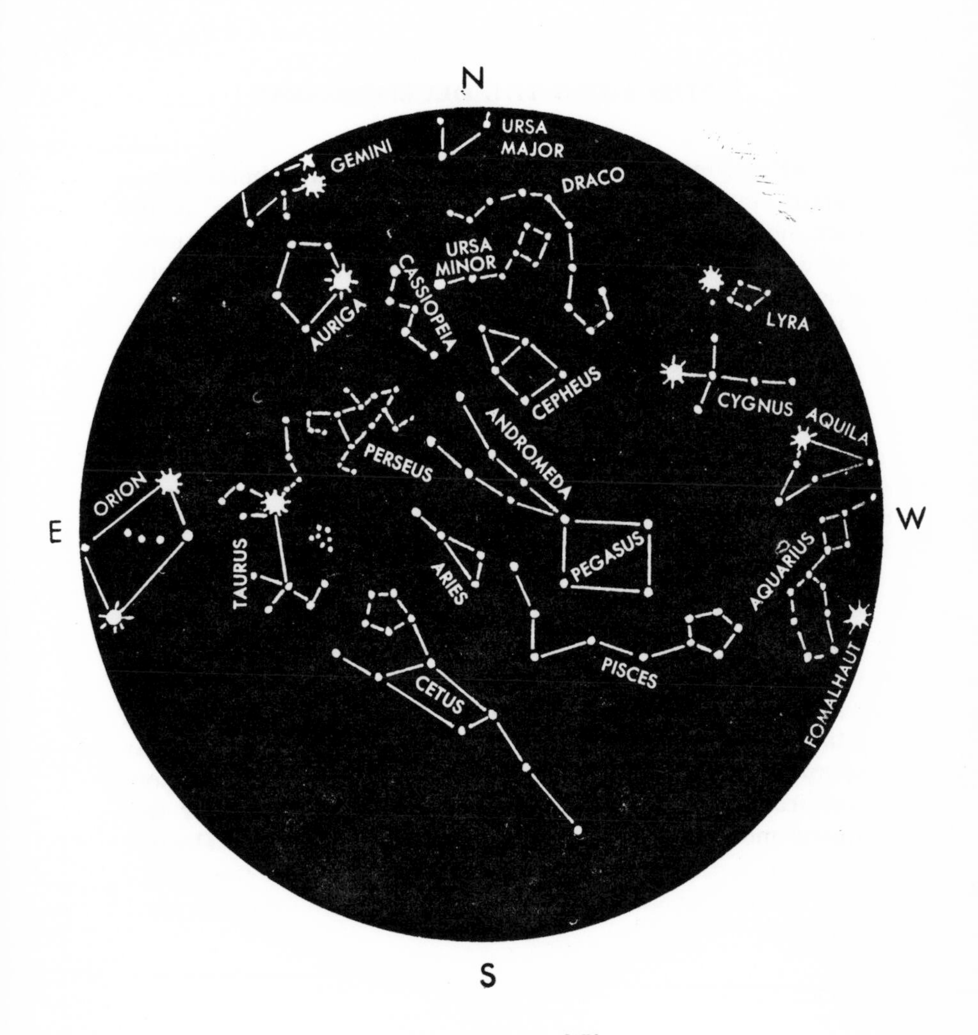

THE NOVEMBER SKY

NOTES FOR THE DECEMBER SKY

The southern sky in December appears almost like a great starles expanse rimming the lower horizon. There are no bright stars to catch the eye and it is with a sense of delight that the observer greets the late rising constellations of Orion and Taurus as they begin to move across this void.

In the east, Procyon, the Little Dog Star shines brightly — a star brighter than the first magnitude. Procyon means "before the dog"; the star's name is derived from the fact that it rises before the Great Dog Star, Sirius comes to dominate the heavens.

In the northern sky the constellation of Draco, twisting its way between the Dippers, is especially easy to observe. It boasts no bright stars and its chief claim as a stellar attraction is its Alpha star, Thuban. The ancient Egyptians thought of Thuban as the North Star. They were not in error as 5,000 years ago the Earth's axis pointed to Thuban and not to Polaris. As a result of this slight "wobble" in the axis of our planet, we can expect that it will again point to Thuban. Calculations indicate that in the year 22,000 A.D. the North Star will once more be Thuban in the constellation of the Dragon.

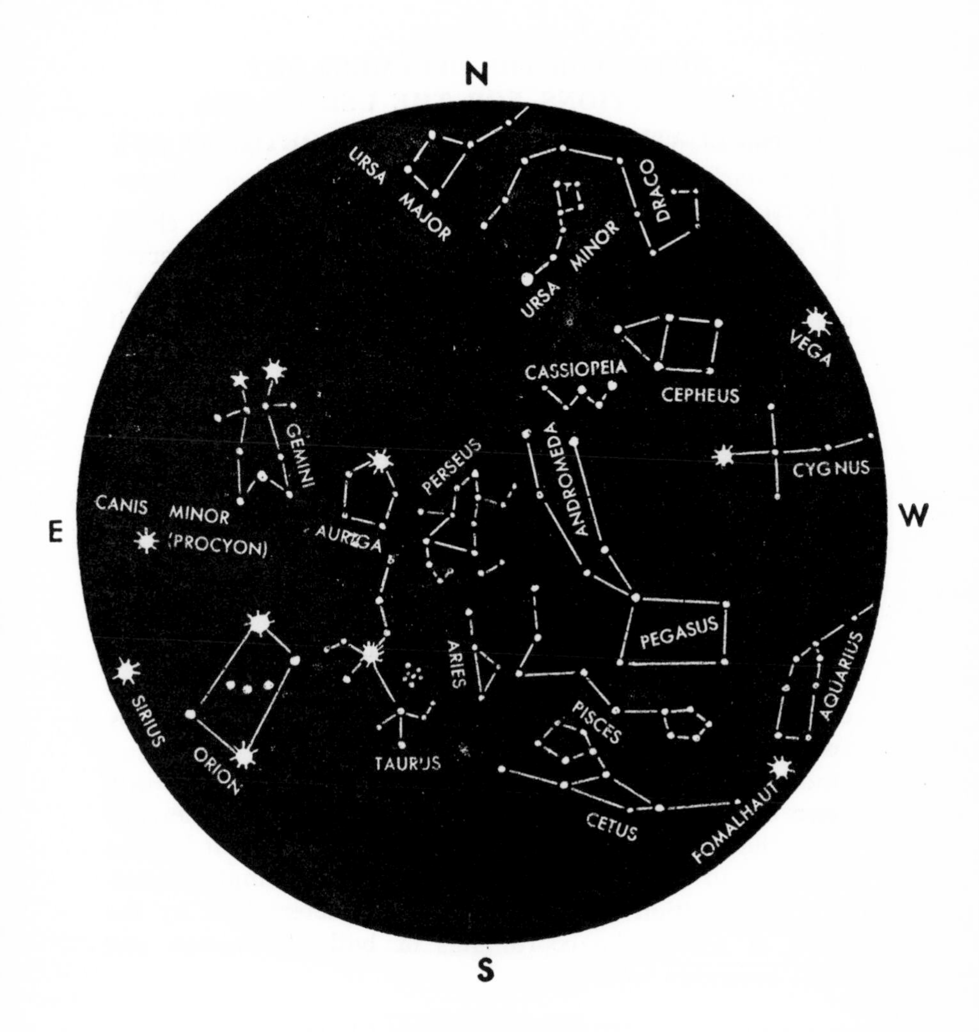

THE DECEMBER SKY

INSTRUCTIONS FOR THE USE OF THE CONSTELLATION CHART OF THE NORTHERN SKY

IN the insert on the rear cover a constellation chart, showing the major constellations visible to an observer in most parts of the United States at some time of the year, has been included. It is removable so that it may be used for outdoor sky studies.

For the sake of simplicity, some minor constellations have been omitted. To that same end the boundaries of the constellations have not been included in this chart. The beginner, however, will find it sufficiently complete and detailed for his use. A list of some of the more advanced star maps and atlases is to be found in the bibliography, and as the sky-watcher gains more experience he will want to refer to these standard works.

The chart is divided by horizontal and vertical scales, divided in intervals of 10°. These scales are parallels of declination and the declination (Dec.) of any star may be read from these scales.

Around the perimeter of the chart the scale divisions have been made in hour circles of sidereal time. On this scale the right ascension of any star may be located. The intervals of right ascension (R.A.) are 15 minutes apart.

The position of any star, then, is determined by the point at which the coordinates of both declination and right ascension intersect.

Orienting The Sky Chart

The chart may be roughly oriented with the sky by holding it overhead and then finding a familiar constellation in the sky and turning the chart so that it relates to the actual star positions that can be seen. The best method, however, is to position the chart by using the sidereal time scale that surrounds it.

If the chart is merely turned around so that the sidereal time at the moment of observation is at the top, then the stars on the chart will be in proper position in relation to the stars in the sky. Of course, this demands that the observer must have a knowledge of sidereal time. There is nothing mysterious about sidereal time; a few moments of study will permit any sky-watcher to use sidereal time as casually as he now employs solar time.

In the table that follows this section, the observer will find that the sidereal time corresponding to 8:00 P.M., Local Time can be read from the table for any day in the year. For example, it is desired to find the sidereal time at 8 o'clock in the evening on February 15th. Referring to the chart, it will be noted that in the February column opposite the 15th day, the value of the sidereal time given is $5^h\ 43^m$.

Now the sky-watcher can orient the star chart by turning it until the value of $5^h\ 43^m$ on the circular scale is at the top. This assumes, of course, that he is observing the sky at 8:00 P.M. If an observation is made at 9:00 P.M., one hour is added to the sidereal time and the value of $6^h\ 43^m$ is turned to the top. At 9:30 P.M., an hour and a half is added giving a value of $7^h\ 13^m$.

Only one other factor remains to be considered — the determination of Local Mean Time. Local Mean Time is, simply speaking, the Standard Time for a specific part of the country with added corrections for the observer's exact position in his time zone. The United States is divided into four time zones. Reading from east to west, these are the Eastern Standard Time Zone, the Central Standard Time Zone, the Mountain Standard Time Zone, and the Pacific Standard Time Zone.

The zones are determined by the time meridians that

run through the center of each zone. Thus, the time meridian for the Eastern Standard Time Zone is the 75° meridian which runs north and south through Philadelphia. In the Central Standard Time Zone, the time meridian is the 90° meridian which passes through St. Louis and New Orleans. The center of the Mountain Standard Time Zone is determined by the 105° meridian which runs through Denver and in the Pacific Standard Time Zone, the 120° meridian runs through Reno, Nevada.

Now, in order to compute Local Mean Time the observer must determine whether his city lies east or west of the time meridian for his zone. This is easily determined by reference to a state map or atlas which will give the longitude for any location in the state. Having obtained the exact longitude for his particular area, the observer is ready to apply the correction that will convert standard time for his zone to an exact value of Local Mean Time.

The correction is determined by adding or subtracting 4 minutes for each degree of longitude that the observer is removed from the time meridian for his zone. For example, the longitude of Green Bay, Wisconsin is 88° 01′. The time meridian for the Central Standard Time Zone is 90° 00′. The observer at Green Bay, then, is 2° (approximately) east of the time meridian. The correction is 4 minutes for each degree removed from the time meridian, and the simple calculation,

2° *times* 4 minutes = 8 minutes, determines the correction. Therefore, at 8:00 P.M. Central Standard Time, the Local Mean Time at Green Bay, Wisconsin is 8:08 P.M.

The corrections are made as follows: If the observer is west of the time meridian, the time correction is *subtracted* from the standard time. If the observer is east of the time meridian the time correction is *added* to the standard time.

Another example will illustrate the application of this method. Let us suppose that an observer at Billings,

Montana wishes to determine the precise Local Mean Time. Billings is in the Mountain Standard Time Zone; the time meridian is the 105° meridian. The observer consults a state map and finds that the exact longitude of Billings, Montana is 108° 30′. This means that the observer's location is 3½° west of the time meridian. The time correction can now be calculated.

3½ *times* 4 = 14 minutes

Because the observer is *west* of the time meridian the time correction must be *subtracted* from the standard time. Thus, at 8:00 P.M. the Local Mean Time at Billings, Montana is 8:00 P.M. *minus* 14 minutes, or 7:46 P.M.

With this information the observer can refer to the table which follows in order to obtain the sidereal time for any day of the year. In this way the fullest and most effective use can be made of the constellation chart.

TABLE SHOWING SIDEREAL TIME AT 8:00 P.M. LOCAL MEAN TIME

DAY	JAN.	FEB.	MARCH	APRIL	MAY	JUNE	JULY	AUG.	SEPT.	OCT.	NOV.	DEC.	DAY
1	2^h 45^m	4^h 48^m	6^h 38^m	8^h 40^m	10^h 39^m	12^h 41^m	14^h 39^m	16^h 41^m	18^h 44^m	20^h 42^m	22^h 44^m	0^h 42^m	1
2	2 49	4 52	6 42	8 44	10 43	12 45	14 43	16 45	18 48	20 46	22 48	0 46	2
3	2 53	4 56	6 46	8 48	10 46	12 49	14 47	16 49	18 51	20 50	22 52	0 50	3
4	2 57	5 00	6 50	8 52	10 50	12 53	14 51	16 53	18 55	20 54	22 56	0 54	4
5	3 01	5 04	6 54	8 56	10 54	12 57	14 55	16 57	18 59	20 58	23 00	0 58	5
6	3 05	5 07	6 58	9 00	10 58	13 01	14 59	17 01	19 03	21 02	23 04	1 02	6
7	3 09	5 11	7 02	9 04	11 02	13 05	15 03	17 05	19 07	21 06	23 08	1 06	7
8	3 13	5 15	7 06	9 08	11 06	13 08	15 07	17 09	19 11	21 09	23 12	1 10	8
9	3 17	5 19	7 10	9 12	11 10	13 12	15 11	17 13	19 15	21 13	23 16	1 14	9
10	3 21	5 23	7 14	9 16	11 14	13 16	15 15	17 17	19 19	21 17	23 20	1 18	10
11	3 25	5 27	7 18	9 20	11 18	13 20	15 19	17 21	19 23	21 21	23 24	1 22	11
12	3 29	5 31	7 22	9 24	11 22	13 24	15 22	17 25	19 27	21 25	23 27	1 26	12
13	3 33	5 35	7 25	9 28	11 26	13 28	15 26	17 29	19 31	21 29	23 31	1 30	13
14	3 37	5 39	7 29	9 32	11 30	13 32	15 30	17 33	19 35	21 33	23 35	1 34	14
15	3 41	5 43	7 33	9 36	11 34	13 36	15 34	17 37	19 39	21 37	23 39	1 38	15
16	3 45	5 47	7 37	9 40	11 38	13 40	15 38	17 40	19 43	21 41	23 43	1 41	16
17	3 49	5 51	7 41	9 43	11 42	13 44	15 42	17 44	19 47	21 45	23 47	1 45	17
18	3 35	5 55	7 45	9 47	11 46	13 48	15 46	17 48	19 51	21 49	23 51	1 49	18
19	3 56	5 59	7 49	9 51	11 50	13 52	15 50	17 52	19 55	21 53	23 55	1 53	19
20	4 00	6 03	7 53	9 55	11 54	13 56	15 54	17 56	19 58	21 57	23 59	1 57	20
21	4 04	6 07	7 57	9 59	11 57	14 00	15 58	18 00	20 02	22 01	0 03	2 01	21
22	4 08	6 11	8 01	10 03	12 01	14 04	16 02	18 04	20 06	22 05	0 07	2 05	22
23	4 12	6 14	8 05	10 07	12 05	14 08	16 06	18 08	20 10	22 09	0 11	2 09	23
24	4 16	6 18	8 09	10 11	12 09	14 12	16 10	18 12	20 14	22 13	0 15	2 13	24
25	4 20	6 22	8 13	10 15	12 13	14 15	16 14	18 16	20 18	22 16	0 19	2 17	25
26	4 24	6 26	8 17	10 19	12 17	14 19	15 18	18 20	20 22	22 20	0 23	2 21	26
27	4 28	6 30	8 21	10 23	12 21	14 23	16 22	18 24	20 26	22 24	0 27	2 25	27
28	4 32	6 34	8 25	10 27	12 25	14 27	16 26	18 28	20 30	22 28	0 31	2 29	28
29	4 36	......	8 29	10 31	12 29	14 31	16 30	18 32	20 34	22 32	0 34	2 33	29
30	4 40	......	8 32	10 35	12 33	14 35	16 33	18 36	20 38	22 36	0 38	2 37	30
31	4 44	......	8 36	......	12 37	......	16 37	18 40	......	22 40	......	2 41	31

Table adapted from the *American Ephemeris*

GLOSSARY OF ASTRONOMICAL TERMS

Achromatic: The characteristic of a lens that permits it to transmit light without dispersal into the component colors that make up the light ray.

ASA rating: The system by which the American Standards Association rates the relative sensitivity of photographic films. High ASA ratings (100 and above) indicate "fast" films and less sensitive films are awarded lower ratings.

Asteroid: An irregularly shaped heavenly body that revolves around the Sun with an orbit between Mars and Jupiter. Smaller than a planet, and, consequently, sometimes known as planetoid.

Astrology: An ancient pseudo-science that attempts to forecast the future by studying the stars and planets that allegedly affect the affairs of men.

Azimuth: A measurement of angle along the celestial horizon from the celestial meridian to the hour circle that passes through the point in question.

Binary star: A pair of relatively close stars revolving about a common center of gravity.

Chromatic aberration: The characteristic of some lenses that causes false and spurious color images, resulting from the inability of the lens to focus light rays of different colors at the same point.

Diffraction pattern: A series of dark and light bands surrounding images at the limit of resolution of an optical system. Patterns are an interference phenomenon resulting from the wave nature of light.

Ecliptic: The path traced out on the celestial sphere by the Sun during its apparent annual journey around the Earth.

Ellipse: A flattened circle resulting from the plane curve traced by the path of a point, the sum of whose distances from a pair of fixed points (foci) is constant.

Ephemeris: A publication of charts and tables showing the positions of the heavenly bodies for each day.

Equinox: The time when the Sun crosses the equator of the celestial sphere resulting in days and nights of equal length. The vernal equinox occurs about March 21 and the autumnal equinox at about September 22.

Galaxy: A vast assemblage of stars in space. An island universe composed of a community of millions of stars.

Geocentric theory: A theory describing the universe as revolving around the Earth as its center. The Ptolemaic theory of antiquity.

Libration: The "rocking" or "wobbling" of a planet or the Moon that permits an observer to see more than one hemisphere of the body.

Luminosity: The quality of radiating or reflecting light.

Mass: A measure of the quantity of matter to be found in any body. Expressed as a function of the body's acceleration due to gravity.

Nebula: An immense, cloudlike mass of gas and dust in space. Appears misty or filmy to the naked eye and to small telescopes.

Nova: A star that undergoes a sudden and intense increase in brightness. Thus, it is as though a "new" star appeared.

Occultation: The passage of one celestial body in front of another with the consequent hiding of the second from view.

Orbit: The path described by one heavenly body as it

revolves about another, i.e., the Moon around the Earth.

Orthoscopic: Characterized by proper seeing. The presentation of an undistorted image to the eye.

Parabolic: Having the shape of a parabola, a curve created by a plane slicing through a cone with the plane parallel to the side of the cone.

Planetary nebula: A gaseous mass in space with the general appearance of a planet when viewed in the telescope.

Prism: A glass body with triangular bases which is used to disperse a beam of light into its spectrum. A prism may also be used to bend a light beam by reflecting it from the surfaces of the prism.

Resolution: The property of an optical system, such as a lens, which permits it to produce separate images of closely spaced objects.

Reticle: Fine lines or cross hairs fixed at the focal plane of an optical instrument to aid in locating an object in the line of sight.

Satellite: A small body which revolves around a planet, such as a moon or an artificial structure which has been placed in an orbit around the larger body.

Solar prominence: An expanding cloud of gas thrusting high above the surface of the Sun. It is best seen when the glare of the Sun's disc is shielded during totality of an eclipse or by instruments.

Spectrohelioscope: A device that permits an observer to study the Sun directly by monochromatic light. The method permits more accurate observation of surface detail and other solar phenomena.

Spectrum: The spreading band of colors formed when a beam of white light is resolved by a prism, or similar device, into its colored components.

Terminator: The boundary line between the illuminated and the unilluminated part of a planet or other heavenly body. Particularly applied to the Moon.

Transit: The passage of a smaller heavenly body across the face of a relatively larger body. For example, the transit of Mercury across the visible disc of the Sun.

Zenith: The point on the celestial sphere directly over the head of the observer.

SUGGESTIONS FOR FURTHER READING

R.H. Baker. *Astronomy.* Princeton: Van Nostrand Co.

R.H. Baker. *Introducing The Constellations.*
New York: Viking Press

R.H. Baker. *When The Stars Come Out.*
New York: Viking Press.

Bernhard, Bennett, and Rice. *New Handbook Of The Heavens.*
New York: McGraw-Hill Book Co.

DeVaucouleurs. *Discovery Of The Universe.*
New York: Macmillan Co.

P. Doig. *A Concise History Of Astronomy.*
London: Chapman & Hill

Fred Hoyle. *The Nature Of The Universe.*
New York: Harper and Brothers.

Fred Hoyle. *Frontiers Of Astronomy.*
New York: Mentor Press.

A.G. Ingalls, ed. *Amateur Telescope Making.*
New York: Scientific American Inc.

Fritz Kahn. *Design Of The Universe.*
New York: Crown Publishers.

H.C. King. *The History of The Telescope.*
Cambridge: Sky Publishing Corp.

R.N. & M. W. Mayall. *Skyshooting.*
New York: Ronald Press.

P. Moore. *A Guide To The Stars.*
New York: W.W. Norton & Co.

H.M. Neely. *A Primer For Star Gazers.*
New York: Harper and Brothers.

C. Payne-Gaposchkin. *Stars In The Making.*
Cambridge: Harvard University Press.

J.S. Pickering. *The Stars Are Yours.*
New York: Macmillan Co.

T. Rackham. *Astronomical Photography At The Telescope.*
New York: Macmillan Co.

H. Shapley. *Galaxies.* Cambridge:
Harvard University Press

J.B. Sidgwick. *Amateur Astronomer's Handbook.*
New York: Macmillan Co.

J.B. Sidgwick. *Observational Astronomy For Amateurs.*
New York: Macmillan Co.

J.B. Sidgwick. *Introducing Astronomy.*
New York: Macmillan Co.

W.M. Smart. *Some Famous Stars.*
New York: Longmans, Green.

A.J. Thompson. *Making Your Own Telescope.*
Cambridge: Sky Publishing Corp.

A SELECTION OF STAR CHARTS AND ATLASES OF THE HEAVENS

Atlas of the Heavens (*Atlas Coeli*) by A. Becvar. Sky Publishing Corp., Cambridge, Mass.

Webb's Atlas of the Stars by H.B. Webb. Lynbrook, N.J.

Norton's Star Atlas and Telescopic Handbook by A.P. Norton & J.G. Inglis. Sky Publishing Corp., Cambridge, Mass.

Field Book of the Skies by Oclott and Mayall. G.G. Putnam's Sons, New York

Celestial Objects For Common Telescopes by T.W. Webb. Dover Publications, New York

The Stars, A New Way To See Them by H.A. Rey. Houghton Mifflin Co., New York

Photographic Lunar Atlas by G.P. Kuiper. Sky Publishing Corp. Cambridge, Mass.

Moon Maps by H.P. Wilkins. Macmillan Co., New York

INDEX

R

S

T

U

– NOTES –

– NOTES –

– NOTES –